Algarve

Text by Neil Schlecht
Updated by Susie Boulton
Edited by Alex Knights
Series Editor: Tony Halliday

C000020404

Berlitz POCKET GUIDE

Algarve

Third Edition 2006

PHOTOGRAPHY CREDITS
All photography by Chris Godet except for:
Chris Coe 10, 12, 20, 82; Mary Evans Picture Library 19; Shaun Botterill/Getty 22; Tony Halliday 73, 74, 75, 77; Pictures Colour Library 89; Cro Magnon/Alamy 91, 96; Stuart Abraham/Alamy 98;
Cover photograph by Neil Schlecht

CONTACTING THE EDITORS
Every effort has been made to provide accurate information in this publication, but changes are inevitable. The publisher cannot be responsible for any resulting loss, inconvenience or injury. We would appreciate it if readers would call our attention to any errors or outdated information by contacting Berlitz Publishing, PO Box 7910, London SE1 1WE, England. Fax: (44) 20 7403 0290;
e-mail: berlitz@apaguide.co.uk
www.berlitzpublishing.com

Sunbathers and beachcombers will appreciate the charms of Falésia beach (page 52), east of Albufeira

Exuberant hand-painted *azulejo* tiles decorate the church of São Lourenço dos Matos (page 55), near Faro

Historic Silves (page 42) was once a Moorish stronghold

TOP TEN ATTRACTIONS

The Igreja de Santo António (page 31) in Lagos is a miniature masterpiece of the baroque

Soak up the atmosphere of Tavira (page 67), one of the most historic cities in the region

Hundreds of monks' skulls and bones line the weird and wonderful Chapel of Bones in Faro's Igreja do Carmo (page 63)

Take a boat trip to see the impressive cliffs, grottoes and rock stacks of the Ponta da Piedade (page 33)

See the catch of the day at Olhão's fascinating fish market (page 65)

Manueline carving at the Igreja Matriz (page 41) , Monchique

The resort of Lagos (page 29) combines a rich history with a busy present

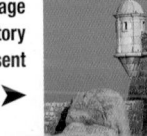

CONTENTS

Fact Sheets

INTRODUCTION

For much of the world, the Algarve is synonymous with Portugal, yet the Portuguese will tell you the exact opposite: the region has little in common with the rest of the country. The southern stretch of coast is more reminiscent of a North African landscape than a European one. It has no cosmopolitan cities, such as Lisbon and Porto, which are further north. Most of Portugal is known for quaint towns, medieval castles and grand palaces. The Algarve is more recognisable for tourist apartments, hotels and golf courses.

And beaches. Think Algarve and the mind pictures long, glorious stretches of golden sands, secluded coves framed by odd ochre-coloured rock formations, and deep green waters. With about 160km (100 miles) of coastline, Portugal's southern province is one of Europe's premier beach destinations. The occasionally chilly ocean is the Atlantic, but the Algarve has a sultry Mediterranean feel.

Apartments in Quarteira

Sun, Sand and Sports

The Algarve's consistent climate is the best in Portugal, and one of the kindest in the world: more than 250 days of sunshine a year – more than almost any other international resort area. The moderating effect of the Gulf Stream produces a fresh springtime breeze throughout winter, and in late January and February, white

A secluded cove in the Western Algarve

almond blossoms blanket the fields. In summer the heat is intense but rarely unbearable, and regardless, beautiful beaches and innumerable pools are always just a drive away.

Magnificent year-round weather has made the Algarve a huge destination for sporting holidays. Superb golf facilities abound – several with tees dramatically clinging to cliffs and fairways just skirting the edge of the ocean – and horse riding, tennis, big-game fishing, sailing and windsurfing are immensely popular.

Sports, beaches and hospitable weather – not to mention easily organised package holidays – are surely the reasons that the Algarve receives as many visitors as the rest of Portugal in its entirety. But it's not just international tourists that descend on the Algarve; many Portuguese from Lisbon and elsewhere in the north have holiday homes and spend their summer holidays here.

A Coastal Province

The coast is neatly divided into the rugged Barlavento to the west and the flat beauty of Sotavento to the east. West is where you'll find the famous orange cliffs and surreal eroded rock stacks. Near Cabo de São Vicente and Sagres, the extreme western point, the terrain is surprisingly barren and the facilities decidedly low-key. The ocean can also be forbiddingly cold.

Tourist resorts clutter the entire middle of the coast, from Lagos to Faro, with a spectrum of homes away

> For centuries, almond, fig, olive and carob trees have represented a major part of Algarve's agriculture, as they are suited to dry inland areas. Thanks to the gentle climate, Algarve also produces pears, apples, quinces, loquats, damask plums, pomegranates, tomatoes, melons, strawberries, avocados and grapes.

Young beachgoers at Praia de Dona Ana

from home – monster high-rises to spacious, single-storey villas – spilling across the rolling hills and lining the beaches. Resorts such as Portimão, Albufeira and Vilamoura would appear to have little room left to grow, yet tourist facilities seem to mate with each other and reproduce overnight. Much of the unstoppable growth is crass and frighteningly commercial, and the crowds in summer unbearable.

The eastern third of the Algarve is a more sedate marriage of coast and ocean, with warm waters and hot sands stretching past the wetlands of Ria Formosa to the Spanish border. The Algarve's most picturesque town, Tavira, is along this section of the coast.

Away from the coast, the terrain slopes through pines, mimosa, eucalyptus and heather to an altitude of nearly 915m (3,000ft). Holidaymakers wishing to escape the maddening beach crowds can run for the hills, especially the tantalising Serra de Monchique.

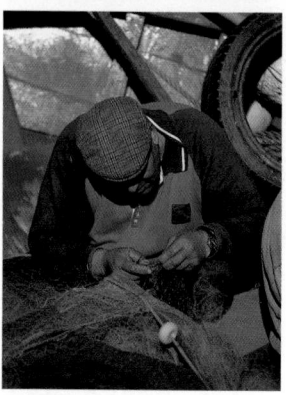

Mending the nets

People of the Sea

The region's exotic name is derived from the Arabic, *Al-Gharb*, meaning 'country of the west'. The westernmost territory of Europe was highly prized by North African Moors, who occupied it from the 8th to the 13th century. Their half millennium here left indelible traces, seen today in whitewashed houses, hill-top castles and colourful ceramic tiles.

Following the recapture of Iberia by Christians, the Algarve led Portugal to glory. Prince Henry the Navigator established his Navigation School along Portugal's southern coast, and intrepid explorers set out in caravels from Lagos and Sagres. In the 15th and 16th centuries, they ushered in an Age of Discovery, rounding Africa's Cape of Good Hope and eventually reaching India and the Pacific. Others found their way to the Americas and Brazil. Opening world trade routes across the globe, they established Portugal as a maritime superpower.

Portugal soon lapsed into decline, though, tattered by wars and constitutional crises, and for two centuries or more the Algarve remained isolated from the rest of Europe. Even though the coast received many illustrious visitors from Roman times through the Middle Ages and up to the Edwardian period (when travellers came to luxuriate in Monchique's spa waters), the Algarve's elite holiday status is a relatively recent phenomenon. The first resort on the coast, Praia da Rocha, was only 'discovered' in the 1930s, and the real build-up didn't kick into overdrive until the early 1980s.

Spain's Costa del Sol developed earlier and more rapidly, yet the lessons of rampant, ill-advised development across the border were not heeded. Only recently has environmental and aesthetic consciousness at least mandated that newer developments are limited in height.

Yet – despite the tourism onslaught – parts of the Algarve retain their old-fashioned charm. The main road along the coast, the N125, is lined with ceramic shops and stifled with summer traffic, but the countryside to the north is a different world. Orchards and grain fields replace hotels, apartments and snack bars. A slow, rural lifestyle perseveres against the rush of modern life.

For centuries, fishing has been the Algarve's lifeblood. Small fishing villages preserve their simple and unaffected ways, seemingly oblivious to the tourist hordes. Scrappy crews of small hand-painted boats troll the waters just offshore, and trawlers fish deep in the Atlantic for big shoals of *bacalhau* (cod), which is beloved by the Portuguese.

A visit to the local fish market is a revealing window into Algarvian life. Negotiations are serious but friendly. The same scenario is played out a thousand times a day at markets all across the region; every town has a market day at least once a month.

Whitewashed houses recall the region's Moorish heritage

Tiled houses in Tavira

Farmers bring their livestock to trade, and artisans and vendors sell their wares.

Not a large area, the Algarve is relatively easy to get around, whether by train or car (an effort that is much more relaxing outside of the main summer season). The distances between megaresorts and unspoiled villages are surprisingly small.

Vestiges of the Past

The Algarve's major attractions, besides beaches, are towns that have lived through centuries of triumph and disaster. Faro, Tavira and Lagos have a strong Moorish influence, and the quiet mountain towns of Silves, Alte and Salir are reminders of the days before golf courses and hotel chains.

Despite the region's ancient roots, few historic monuments survive from before 1755, when the Algarve was rocked by a monumental earthquake. Still, you'll find vestiges of a vibrant past, including evocative castle ruins and churches with extraordinary displays of Portuguese glazed tiles. Even the humblest village has a classic white church, a sleepy plaza shaded by vivid purple jacaranda, and, if you time it right, the drama of the local market.

The Portuguese are famously hospitable, if reserved. And they remain tolerant and helpful, even though they know that their lovely coast is no longer just theirs.

A BRIEF HISTORY

L ittle is known of the earliest Stone Age inhabitants of Europe's southwestern extremity. The ancient Greeks called them the Cynetes (or Cunetes). Whatever their origins, their culture evolved under the pressure and influence of foreign forces. Among the many invading armies that settled here and contributed to nascent Portuguese culture were Phoenicians, who settled in the area around 1000BC, followed by the Celts, Iberians, Greeks and Carthaginians.

But it was the Romans, who arrived late in the 3rd century BC, who most greatly influenced Iberia. They built towns, roads and bridges, developed industries and agriculture, and bequeathed the Latin language, of which Portuguese is a descendant. The Romans named the southwestern province of the peninsula Lusitania, after one of the Celtiberian tribes they had defeated, and by the 3rd century AD had introduced Christianity. By the early 4th century the Algarve had a bishop in place, based in Faro. But Rome had fallen into decay, and soon hordes of northern tribesmen took over the empire. The Algarve fell to the Visigoths in the mid-5th century.

Waterwheel and wells are a legacy of the Moors

Under Moorish Rule

In AD711, the Moors brought powerful armies from North Africa and launched a devastating attack on the Iberian peninsula, conquering much of what would become Spain and Portugal. They imposed Islam and left an indelible in-

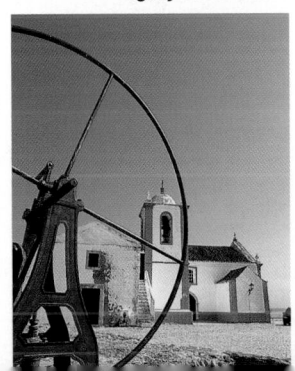

fluence on the countryside and population of the Algarve. The Moorish legacy can still be seen in the form of wells and water-wheels, squat white houses, the dark complexions of the people and in the very name of the region – taken from Al-Gharb, which means 'country of the west' (when the Moors conquered the territory, it was the most westerly in the known world).

The Moors governed their Iberian kingdoms from across the border in Seville, but the Algarve had its own regional capital and huge, invulnerable fortress. The capital was Chelb (or Xelb), and it was bigger and better defended than Lisbon. Today the town, known as Silves *(see page 42)*, is a provincial outpost whose only besiegers are busloads of tourists.

The fortress at Castro Marim

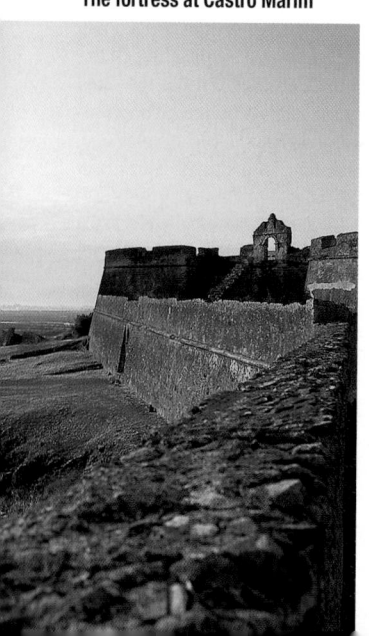

The struggle by Christians to expel the Moors (a campaign known as the *Reconquista*, or Reconquest) began in the late 8th century AD. By the 11th century, Portucale consisted of a small section of territory previously held by Castile and León (which became today's northern Portugal). Yet it wasn't until the 12th century that significant gains were made to take back southern Iberia. The beginning of the end came in the Battle of Ourique in 1139. After the victory, Count Afonso Henriques proclaimed himself the first king of Portugal, making it one of the first nation-states in Europe.

The Reconquest of Silves, not achieved for another 50 years, was a grisly affair. A mixed bag of Crusaders from northern Europe were recruited en route to their battles east in the Holy Land. They sailed upon the river port of Silves and, ignoring conditional offers of surrender, slew all the inhabitants (at no small loss to themselves) and pillaged the great treasures of the city.

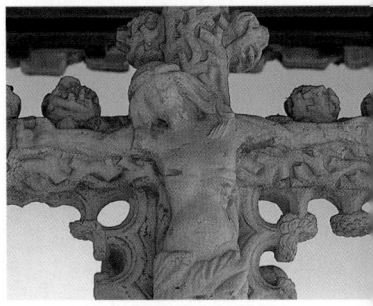

Ultimately, the Christian influence prevailed in Silves

Two years later Muslim forces rallied again, retaking Silves, and the *Reconquista* stumbled on for another half century. So many inter-religious alliances reigned, and so pervasive was the intermingling of Moors and Christians, that it was hard to tell who was on which side and for which piece of land they were fighting. The situation was further clouded by a feud between Portugal and Spain, each of them claiming sovereignty over the Algarve. However, by 1249 Faro and the western Algarve were retaken under King Afonso III, completing the *Reconquista*. The possibility of war with Spain was averted by an expeditious royal marriage, and at the century's close a treaty with Spain drew up the boundaries of Portugal that stand today.

The Algarve was a region regarded separately within the new Portugal, as is evidenced by the royal title 'Kingdom of Portugal and the Algarve'. In those days, the notion of the Algarve as a distinct entity did make some sense: like an island, it was cut off to the south and west by the Atlantic, to the east by the Guadiana River, and to the north by the Serra de Monchique mountain range. The region's titular autonomy was upheld until 1910, when the monarchy itself was overthrown.

Henry the Navigator

In 1415, long after the *Reconquista* was completed, a Portuguese fleet assembled on the River Tagus in Lisbon, ready for an assault on the Moors in their homeland. Crossing the Straits of Gibraltar, the armada attacked and seized the North African city of Ceuta. An illustrious member of the famous raid was the young Prince Henry – half Portuguese and half English – and the son of King João I and his wife, Philippa of Lancaster. Ceuta would be Henry's one and only military victory, though he was destined to establish Portugal as a major world power, helping to develop important world trade routes by the time of his death in 1460.

The waters at the western extreme of the Algarve were all that was known to sailors. Once they were beyond Cabo de São Vicente, they faced the unknown, with no communications and no possibility of rescue if the voyage turned out badly. Yet out into the unknown they went; for the glory of God and

School of Navigation

At the age of 21, Henry assembled a School of Navigation. It was certainly not a formal institution of lectures and classes, but probably resembled an informal modern-day 'think-tank'. Prince Henry – made governor of the Algarve in 1418 – had the money, influence, enthusiasm and vision to lead and cajole the best astronomers, cartographers, boat-designers and seamen of the day to expand Portugal's maritime horizons.

According to tradition, the site of Prince Henry's base was the Sagres peninsula *(see page 25)*, though there is little there today to persuade you of this. The actual headquarters of the Navigation School may have been 40km (25 miles) east, in Lagos *(see page 29)*. This location had a port, shipyards and was home to the prince in his role as governor of the Algarve.

country, and in search of personal fame and fortune. Their mission was made easier by the craft Algarve shipwrights had developed, a successor to the lumbering ships of the day: the caravel. It was light, fast and very manoeuvrable. With the subsequent development of new navigational techniques, it was no longer necessary to stay within sight of land. Now the only limits to maritime exploration were man's ingenuity and courage.

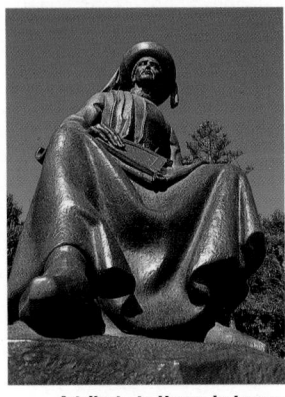

A tribute to Henry in Lagos

During Henry's lifetime, Portugal's caravels sailed beyond the most westerly point of Africa. They colonised the Atlantic islands of Madeira and the Azores, laying the foundations for the future Portuguese Empire. Before the century was over, Henry's compatriots Bartolomeu Dias and Vasco da Gama completed epic voyages, rounding the Cape of Good Hope and reaching India, respectively, and Pedro Álves Cabral claimed Brazil. Between 1519 and 1522 another Portuguese explorer, Ferdinand Magellan, led the first expedition to circumnavigate the world. Mercantilist Portugal became a rich maritime superpower.

Foreign Intrigues

To protect its seagoing interests and trade routes, Portugal established strategic garrisons in Goa (India), Malacca (East Indies) and Hormuz in the Persian Gulf. Portuguese explorers then embarked upon Macau (now Macao), the Congo and various other parts of Africa, including the Sudan. The Portuguese policy was to avoid armed strife and to develop a trade empire,

> For many years after his death, legends and rumours bizarrely insisted that King Sebastião was still alive, and imposters turned up from time to time claiming the throne; those who were plausible enough to be deemed a threat were summarily executed.

rather than to conquer nations. To this end it succeeded with relatively few blood-soaked episodes in its colonial history.

Adventures abroad, however, proved disastrous during the second half of the 16th century. In 1557 the 14-year-old boy-king Sebastião ascended the throne, the beginning of a calamitous reign that was to end at the battle of Alcacer-Quiber (Morocco) in pursuit of a vain crusade. Sebastião's untimely demise, alongside some 18,000 ill-prepared, badly led followers, set the stage for a crisis of succession.

The only rightful claimant to the crown was an elderly prince, Henry. But after two years of alternating between the throne and his sickbed, he died, heirless. Spain, sensing an opportunity, occupied the power vacuum, and Portugal's neighbour and long-time antagonist became its master.

Spanish rule dictated Portugal's inadvertent involvement in Spain's ongoing wars. In 1587 a squadron of English ships commanded by Francis Drake attacked the Algarve (now a 'legitimate target' as Spanish territory) and sacked Sagres, thus depriving the world of the relics of Henry the Navigator. Nine years later Faro was torched by command of the Earl of Essex. The 1386 Treaty of Windsor, by which England and Portugal had pledged eternal friendship, seemed a distant memory.

Portugal's empire was gradually eroded, and many of its trading posts (with the exception of Brazil) were picked off by the English and Dutch. Finally, after 60 years of Spanish rule, Portuguese noblemen (aided by the French, then at war with Spain) organised a palace coup and restored independence.

The Great Disaster

Portugal's greatest misfortune struck on All Saints' Day, 1 November 1755. With candlelit churches crowded with worshippers, an earthquake struck, followed by fast-spreading fires and a devastating tidal wave that swept over the Algarve as far as 6.5km (4 miles) inland. The exact casualty figure will never be known, but it is estimated that 5,000 died immediately and between 40,000 and 60,000 perished as a result of secondary injuries and the ensuing famine and pestilence. The epicentre of the earthquake is thought to have been off the Algarve coast, possibly between Tavira and Faro, but it devastated places as far away as the capital, Lisbon.

Throughout the Algarve and much of the rest of southern Portugal, virtually every important monument, cathedral, castle and mansion was destroyed, or at least critically damaged in the earthquake. Among the hardest-hit towns was

The effects of the earthquake were felt as far away as Lisbon

Lagos *(see page 29)* which lost its castle, its churches and the palace in which Henry the Navigator had once lived.

Political Upheaval

The beginning of the 19th century brought further alarm. This time the epicentre was Paris, and the cause of the problems, Napoleon. Just as Portugal's forced alliance with Spain had made the country a target for Drake's 16th-century raids, now her friendly alliance with Britain rankled Napoleon.

In 1807 the French invaded Lisbon, causing the royal family to flee to Brazil. Spain, followed by Portugal, rose up against the French occupation, in what came to be known as the Peninsular War. Among the early blows struck for independence was a rebellion in the town of Olhão *(see page 64)*. On 16 June 1808, the townsfolk – armed with little more than ancient swords, spears and stones – attacked and captured the local French garrison. The real battle, however, was waged under the leadership of the Duke of Wellington, whose coalition forces expelled the French after two years of bitter fighting.

The war left Portugal further weakened, and in 1822 its major empire outpost, Brazil, declared independence. At the same time, a dispute over the crown con-

Cape St Vincent

tinually raged between Pedro IV, the absentee monarch who preferred to reign as Emperor of Brazil rather than return to Portugal, and his brother Miguel. The power struggle, with strong overtones of absolutism versus liberalism, excited the interest and intervention of other powers. With British help, Pedro defeated Miguel off Cape St Vincent in 1833, and his expeditionary force marched to Lisbon. Pedro took the throne, though armed struggle continued for months.

By 1892 Portugal, racked by wars and the continuing expense of maintaining its African colonies (including those of Mozambique and Angola), declared itself bankrupt. The seeds of discontent with absolutist rule were sown.

Kingdom's End

On 1 February 1908, the royal family was riding in an open carriage along the Lisbon riverfront plaza, Terreiro do Paço, when an assassin opened fire and killed King Carlos and the heir to the throne, Prince Luis Filipe. The prince's younger brother, Prince Manuel, was also hit, but he survived and was thus propelled to the throne at the tender age of 19. Amid republican agitation, a surprise uprising led by elements within the armed forces deposed Manuel in 1910.

The sudden end of more than seven centuries of monarchy brought confusion and crisis to the country. Presidents and prime ministers were ushered into and out of office an unbelievable 45 times between 1910 and 1926, until a military revolution suspended Portugal's problematic democracy. After six years of power, General Oscar Carmona appointed his finance minister, António de Oliveira Salazar, to be prime minister, a position he was to hold until 1968. Salazar's repressive rule and austerity measures rid the Portuguese economy of debt, though poverty increased. Portugal remained neutral during World War II, and Salazar demonstrated his financial acumen by selling materials and supplies to both sides.

In 1968 the elderly Salazar was forced into retirement after a stroke. His successor, Dr Marcelo Caetano, feeling the spirit of the age, began tentative relaxations of the old regime. The armed forces finally overthrew him in a popular bloodless coup, known as the 'Carnation Revolution', on 25 April 1974.

Portugal finally began to pull itself out of the long and fruitless struggle against revolutionaries in its African colonies, and granted independence to the remaining members of its empire in 1975. This, too, caused major upheavals, and a million permanent refugees rushed to the motherland, aggravating the shortage of housing and jobs.

Although economic problems continued to beset the young democracy, the political scene was greatly stabilised. In 1986 Portugal, the former poor backwater of Europe, joined the European Economic Community (now the European Union, or EU).

With aid from the EU, Portugal became one of the fastest-growing countries in Europe. The Algarve, already a favourite of sun-seeking beach lovers from the UK and northern Europe, also benefited from EU funds to build up its infrastructure and to invest in tourism. In 1998 Portugal hosted the World Expo in Lisbon. In January 2000 it was among the first group of EU members to enter the single currency, with the euro introduced in 2002. In 2004 Portugal hosted the European Football Championships, Faro's new stadium, Estadio do Algarve, staging the first-round matches.

A sign of the country's growing wealth, the Estadio do Algarve

Historical Landmarks

c. **1000BC** Phoenicians settle in the Algarve region.
700BC Celtic tribes arrive.
205BC Romans create Lusitania province.
5th century Algarve falls to the Visigoths.
711 Moors arrive on the Iberian peninsula and swiftly conquer it.
883 Northern Portugal (Portucale) regained by Christian forces.
1139 Count Afonso Henriques declares himself first king of Portugal.
1147 Lisbon taken by Afonso Henríques.
1189 Silves taken by the Christians; regained by the Moors 1191.
1249 Moors are finally expelled from the Algarve.
1386 Treaty of Windsor confirms England–Portugal alliance.
1415 The Atlantic island of Madeira reached by explorers under the patronage of Henry the Navigator, starting the Age of Discoveries.
1498 Vasco da Gama opens a sea route to India.
1500 Pedro Álvares Cabral reaches Brazil.
1580 Portugal falls under Spanish rule for 60 years.
1587 English fleet sacks Sagres.
1755 The Great Earthquake devastates the towns of the Algarve, as well as Lisbon.
1807 Napoleonic troops invade Portugal at the start of the Peninsular War; royal family leaves for Brazil.
1829–34 Civil war between Pedro IV and Miguel I.
1892 Portugal declares itself bankrupt.
1908 King Carlos I and Prince Luis Filipe assassinated.
1910 Monarchy overthrown; Portugal becomes a republic.
1932 António de Salazar becomes prime minister and effective dictator.
1974 The Carnation Revolution restores democracy; Portugal pulls out of African colonies and a million expatriates return.
1986 Portugal joins the European Economic Community (now the EU).
1998 Lisbon hosts Expo '98.
2002 The euro replaces the escudo as the national currency.
2004 Portugal hosts the European Football Championship.

WHERE TO GO

The Algarve stretches from the Atlantic Ocean to Spain, but it's actually a small region. Faro, the capital, is just 50km (30 miles) from the Spanish border, and it is only 112km (70 miles) west of what was known in medieval times as *o fim do mundo* (the end of the world) at Sagres. Along this 160-km (100-mile) coastal strip, resorts and holiday villages of all types have sprung up, so wherever you are based, you'll never be far from a good beach, a reasonably sized town, village, or resort, shops and nightlife.

The following pages cover the Algarve from west to east, though you could certainly do the reverse or begin in the centre, in or around Faro, and embark on day trips both east and west from there. For those with additional time and an interest in seeing the Portuguese capital, a brief section on Lisbon is included. Lisbon is about two to three hours by car (and 40 minutes by plane) from Faro; it should be conceived as an add-on to your visit to the Algarve rather than a day trip. Many people visit the Algarve by flying into Lisbon and driving to the south coast. If you are flying directly to Faro and wish to spend a few days in Lisbon, it would make sense to see about a return flight from there. For indepth coverage of Lisbon's main sights and attractions, along with detailed hotel and restaurant listings, we recommend *Berlitz Pocket Guide Lisbon*.

WESTERN ALGARVE

The Sagres Peninsula

If you begin your journey at **Sagres**, you may be in for a shock. The stark town and area around it scarcely look the part

Fishing boats in Lagos harbour

of a fabled beach resort with a Mediterranean feel. Rather, it is remote, rugged and desert-like, with only a relative smattering (compared to the rest of the Algarve) of hotels, restaurants and other facilities aimed at tourists. It is like the Algarve's outpost, which is precisely why it has so many admirers.

Sagres' connections to the sea are strong. Prince Henry the Navigator established his Navigation School here (though some protest that it was further east, near Lagos). The town has a picturesque working harbour, where small, brightly painted fishing boats bob and larger vessels haul in daily catches of lobster, eel and mackerel. A couple of restaurants are clustered around the harbour, with impressive views. Inland, a cute little square, Praça República, is ringed by informal (and, in summer, heaving) nightspots.

The best beaches near Sagres are sheltered and not overcrowded. **Mareta**, down below the *pousada* (government-

Telheiro Beach on the west coast

owned inn), is the most popular. **Martinhal**, just east of the harbour, is a wide, curved beach with a first-class water-sports centre. **Beliche** (also written Belixe) is a sandy expanse protected by the Cape of St Vincent. **Tonel**, just before Beliche, and **Telheiro**, about 9km (6 miles) up the west coast from Sagres, are also well-regarded beach spots.

Henry the Navigator – Infante Dom Henrique – was bequeathed the land around Sagres in 1443 by his brother. Henry lived within the castle and died in Sagres in 1460, though his remains were later transferred to the Batalha monastery north of Lisbon.

Beyond the village of Sagres, a great, rocky peninsula hangs above a brooding ocean. You'll understand why, in the days before the great Portuguese explorers set out from here seeking to discover the great beyond, it was known as the End of the World. Those wishing to put a positive spin on things called it Sacrum Saturni – Holy Promontory – and believed that the gods slept here.

Since time immemorial this forlorn place has stirred the imagination. It shook Henry and his sailors, who are said to have set up camp at the **Fortaleza de Sagres** (Fortress) that sits on the promontory. Unfortunately, not much of the original has survived. Most of it is a 17th-century fort that was insensitively restored. In 1991, the walls of this monument were resurfaced with grey concrete, masking the external character of the building. The fortress's principal building, which may have been Henry's headquarters, no longer exists. What you'll find inside is a small 16th-century chapel, Nossa Senhora da Graça, and what looks to be a huge stone sundial, known as the **Rosa dos Ventos** (Rose Compass). Whether, in fact, it was a wind compass useful in the great voyages is unknown. A modern hall on the fort's grounds houses an exhibition area.

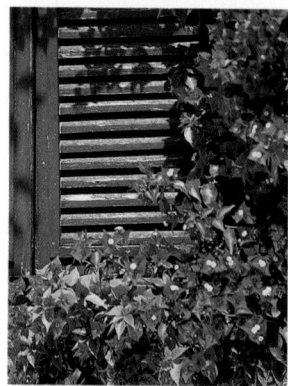

Shutting out the world in sleepy Burgau

A couple of kilometres (1 mile) west of Sagres are the more authentic remains of another fortress, **Fortaleza do Beliche**. This small, attractive 17th-century castle houses a white, domed chapel (Santa Catarina) and is home to a smart traditional-style restaurant. Both the fort and chapel, however, threaten to collapse because the surrounding cliffs are eroding at a frightening rate. Efforts to shore up the cliffs and save the historic site have recently been undertaken.

The windswept cliffs of **Cabo de São Vicente**, the most southwesterly point in Europe, were once surely even more bleak than they are today, when supertankers and small yachts heave into view around the cape. But even on the calmest of days, the Atlantic thunders below and the wind whips around the cape. At the tip of the point, the lighthouse, built in 1904 on the site of a convent chapel, has a beam visible up to 96km (60 miles) away. Visitors can climb the stairs to a hot, enclosed lookout.

The first settlement of any size outside Sagres is **Vila do Bispo**, situated 7km (4 miles) to the north. Take a break in the peaceful town's pleasant, flower-filled garden square and pay a visit to the 18th-century parish church. The walls are covered with *azulejos* (tiles) and the ceiling decorated with frescoes.

About halfway between Sagres and Lagos, **Salema** is regarded as an up-and-coming resort of this stretch, with a lively sprinkling of bars and restaurants, a pleasant beach with fishing boats and a market.

Burgau, 3.2km (2 miles) east, is small and sleepy. Fishing boats pulled up onto the end of the road leading down to the beach jostle with cars. The beach here is less attractive than those at neighbouring Luz or Salema, but the small village retains its easygoing character.

Luz is a pleasant seaside town. All that remains of old Luz is the church and, opposite, the **fortress**, which has been renovated and converted into a restaurant. There is a good beach with water-sports facilities and large, flat rocks for sunbathing.

Lagos

The principal resort of the western Algarve, **Lagos** is the rare beach town that offers something for everyone. By night Lagos is lively, with outdoor restaurant terraces and bars

Dusk falls on Lagos' main street, the Rua 25 de Abril

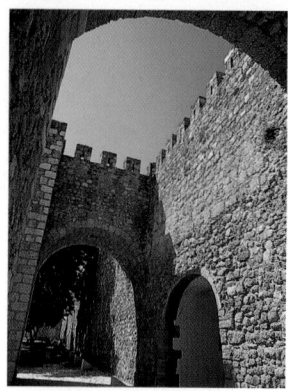

Forte da Ponte da Bandeira

attracting a hipper crowd than most resorts on the coast, and by day it combines a rich historical past with a busy present. Attractive beaches are just on the outskirts of town, so it is not a classic resort in the style of Praia da Rocha.

Your first view of Lagos will probably be from the long, riverside Avenida dos Descobrimentos, which divides the old walled city from the port. At the other end of the avenue, the well-restored fortress, **Forte da Ponte da Bandeira**, guarded the entrance to the harbour in the 17th century. Cross the river to see busy fishermen, handsome boats anchored in the marina and the fine view of the city above the walls. Many of the streets rising towards the top of town are narrow, cobbled and more accustomed to donkeys than rental cars. Though Lagos town still retains a good part of its original walls – most of them from the 16th century, but part-Roman in places – they have been rebuilt and expanded over the centuries. Climb the ramparts for fine views over the port and out to sea.

Lagos was an important trading port under the Moors, but the town enjoyed its heyday after the Christian Reconquest. It was proclaimed the capital of the Algarve, and the governor's palace became the headquarters of Prince Henry. A formal statue of Henry, seated with sextant in hand, has been erected on Praça Dom Henrique next to the main avenue. Arguments persist over the exact whereabouts of the prince's School of Navigation, but it seems almost certain that Lagos was the principal shipyard and port serving his team of explorers.

Those were glory years, but some of what was glorious in those heady times today can seem reprehensible. Explorations along the west coast of Africa in the mid-15th century established a flourishing slave trade, and Lagos was a key player in human commerce. Just behind the statue of Henry, on the corner of Rua da Senhora da Graça, you can still see the small arcade where Portugal's first slave auctions took place. A small plaque states simply **Mercado de Escravos** (Slave Market). Most other historic buildings around the square succumbed to the devastating earthquake of 1755 *(see page 19)*. The majority of the city's attractive buildings thus date from the late 18th and 19th centuries.

On Rua General Alberta da Silveira, the tiny **Igreja de Santo António**, an exuberant gilt baroque work and one of the Algarve's finest churches, was rebuilt soon after the earthquake. The church, a national monument dedicated to St Anthony, has a handsome display of 18th-century blue-and-white glazed tiles and a brightly painted wooden ceiling. Set into the floor you'll find the tomb of an Irish colonel, Hugh Beatty, a soldier of fortune who commanded the Lagos Regiment

Igreja de Santo António

of the Portuguese Army in the late 18th century, and who must have been held in very high esteem to have been awarded such a prestigious final resting place.

The entrance to the church is through the curious and eclectic museum next door, the **Museu Regional de Lagos** (open Tues–Sun 9.30am–12.30pm and 2–5pm; admission fee; tel: 282-76 23 01). Rooms display sacred art, archaeological remains, the original charter of Lagos, holy vestments and a bizarre collection of creatures, like a science experiment gone wrong: an eight-legged goat kid preserved in formaldehyde, a one-eyed sheep, a cat with two faces.

The main street of Lagos is the charming, cobbled **Rua 25 de Abril**, packed with restaurants, bars and antiques and ceramics shops. The side streets hold some good art and craft galleries and plenty of rewards for exploration. The square at the end of 25 de Abril holds a curious statue, which some liken to an extraterrestrial, of the boy-king Sebastião. In 1568 Sebastião became king of Portugal at the age of 14. A decade later he embarked on a disastrous voyage to Morocco to fight the Moors. At least 7,000 troops died, the king included (though many refused to believe he had perished, and Elvis-like sightings were common).

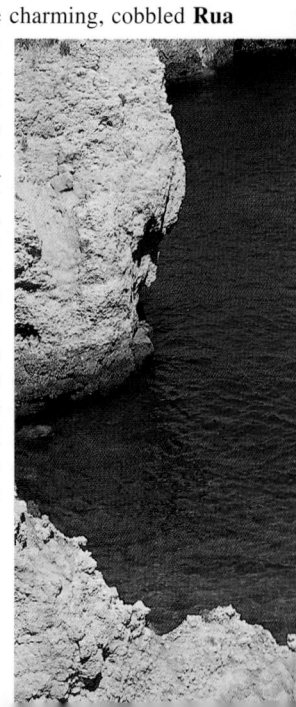

Spectacular rock formations at the Ponta da Piedade

The Coast Around Lagos

The beaches near Lagos range from **Meia Praia**, 1.6km (1 mile) to the east, a long (4km/2½ mile) flat stretch, to pocket-sized coves just west of the city. Weird and wonderful rock formations, and steep cliffs that glow orange at sunset, have made them some of the most photographed in Europe; head for **Praia de Dona Ana** and **Praia do Camilo**, both small, pretty and crowded (street signs show the way to each).

At the southern tip, just before it turns west to Sagres, are the coast's most spectacular sights. **Ponta da Piedade** (Point of Piety) is the mother of all stack and cliff formations along

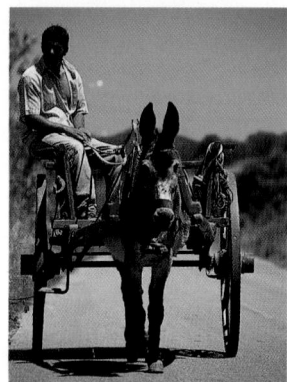

Traditional ways of life endure in the land around Bensafrim

the Algarve, a stunning terracotta family of bridges, terraces and grottoes. There is no beach here, but there are great views from above, and in season (spring to autumn) boat trips depart from the foot of the steps that have been cut deep into the sides of the cliff.

Northwest of Lagos

For a complete change of scene, take a drive northwest towards the hills and **Bensafrim**. Here you can enjoy the Algarve of yesteryear and rolling undeveloped countryside, where people still live off the land. The tilled soil, a startling ochre colour, makes a bright backdrop for orange and lemon groves. Turn off towards the **Barragem da Bravura** and you'll be rewarded with a sight every bit as inspiring as its name. This body of water, more akin to the English Lake District than sunny southern Europe, is of great practical use, irrigating crops, including rice, around Lagos. A new road (N120) connects with the old N125 route and will undoubtedly open up this relatively undeveloped area.

Portimão

Second in size only to Faro in the Algarve, **Portimão** is the most workmanlike town on the coast. But nestled around it are some of the Algarve's finest beaches, which has transformed the town into one of the coast's most popular resorts. Praia da Rocha and Praia Três Irmãos in particular are lined with hotels. Most holidaymakers stay along this stretch.

Portimão sits at the confluence of the River Adade and the sea, and most of its local colour is down by the port, a haven of fishing activity. The top fish-canning spot on the Algarve, Portimão is renowned for its restaurants specialising in *sardinhas grelhadas* (grilled sardines). Though Portimão was settled by the Romans, it was one of the Algarve towns most damaged from the earthquake of 1755, and as a consequence has few buildings or monuments of historical interest. **Largo 1° de Dezembro** is a 19th-century addition, a park with 10 splendid blue-and-white *azulejo* benches, each illustrating a pivotal event in the history of Portugal. The park's name alludes to the date, 1 December 1640, when Portugal's independence from Spain was restored (see page 18).

Much of the town centre is pedestrian-only and filled with shops. The main square, at Rua do Comércio and Avenida São João de Deus, is where you'll find the large

Catching the rays on one of Portimão's golden beaches

Apartments in the popular resort of Portimão

and austere **Colégio dos Jesuítas** (Jesuit College). The church, constructed at the end of the 17th century, is the largest on the Algarve.

Around the corner, along Rua Machado dos Santos, is the handsome **Igreja de Nossa Senhora da Conceição**, sitting atop a small hill and incline of steps. The yellow-and-white church, originally constructed in the 15th century, has a beautiful Gothic portico with carved capitals, but looks like a colonial church you might find in Brazil, due to its reconstruction and remodelling during the 18th and 19th centuries.

From the centre of town, head to the waterfront, especially if it's anywhere near time for lunch or dinner. You can almost follow your nose towards the heady aroma of grilled sardines. It will take you to the **dockside**, which is lined with simple restaurants, one after the other, all serving delicious, smoky sardines (and other freshly caught fish). Choose whichever spot seems to be bustling with ravenous patrons.

A plate of grilled sardines, prawns or squid and a bottle of house wine make a fantastic meal, and the prices are about as low as anywhere along the coast.

The hectic operations of the fishing industry used to take place here right under the noses of holidaymakers, with a frenetic 'bucket-brigade' hauling wicker baskets of fresh fish up from the boat holds to ice trays and waiting trucks, right next to dockside dining tables. The fishermen have now been moved to a larger location on the other side of the river, but most sightseeing boats that tour the harbour and nearby grottoes include a quick trip to the new docks. You will still see fishing boats at anchor on the main quay, but the majority of river traffic here now is made up of private yachts, replica sailing ships on tourist excursions and tiny dinghies.

Portimão's other claim to fame is its status as a comprehensive regional shopping centre. There is certainly a good variety of shops here, including many international names,

Fishy Business

At night out on the ocean, a couple of kilometres or so beyond the beach, you may see tiny specks of light glinting below the stars. These are the lanterns of a small fleet of fishing boats in a wide formation, luring fish into an elaborate net. For centuries fishing has been big business in the Algarve, but the biggest boom began 100 years ago when the canning industry came to the region. To this day, thousands of tonnes of fish, mostly sardines, with tuna coming in a close second, are caught, tinned and exported annually.

Those who have tasted plump and juicy sardines fresh from the quay at Portimão or elsewhere in the Algarve – they're best in summer, when mature – can only feel a little sorry for those who have to take their pleasures many weeks later, from a tin. If you're in Portimão during August, check out the Sardine Festival.

as well as outlets selling traditional crafts or locally made items. A market is often set up in the square opposite the Colégio dos Jesuítas.

Praia da Rocha

Just 3km (2 miles) down river from Portimão is **Praia da Rocha**, which became a holiday village for wealthy Portuguese families at the end of the 19th century. It was 'discovered' by the British in the 1930s, when this 'beach of rocks', strewn with extravagantly shaped eroded stacks, provided an inspirational refuge for writers and intellectuals. The belle-époque Hotel Bela Vista is a surviving monument from those days.

Today the 2-km (1.3-mile) long golden **beach** is still the main attraction, but the once-small village fronting the beach has been swamped by a sea of hotels and tourist facilities.

A peaceful moment at the busy resort of Praia da Rocha

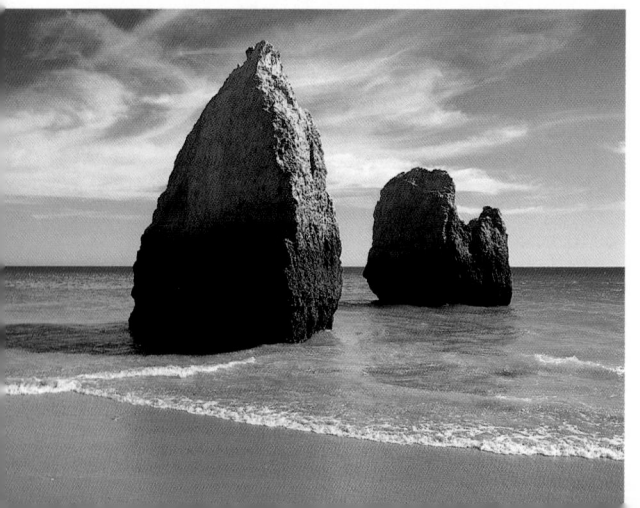

Vestiges of the village's former grandeur can still be traced along the front, where grand old buildings jostle uncomfortably with high-rise blocks. The sprawl has entirely blurred Praia da Rocha's separate identity from Portimão.

At the far eastern end of the resort, guarding the River Arade, is the **Fortaleza de Santa Catarina de Ribamar** (St Catherine's Fortress), built in 1621 to defend Silves and Portimão against the Moors. Little remains of the actual fortress, but its courtyard is now an agreeable terrace where you can enjoy a drink and watch the sardine fleet returning to port. Directly across from the fort is the splendid, beige-coloured **Fortaleza de Ferragudo**, which looks like a giant sandcastle; note that this is closed to the public.

The old fishing village of **Ferragudo** nearby is well worth a visit. Despite its proximity to a main tourist enclave, and two excellent beaches of its own, it has resisted blatant commercialisation, remaining a traditional fishermen's settlement. The opposite end of Praia da Rocha's long stretch is known as **Praia do Vau**. The splendid rock formations and coves continue, but this end of the beach is quieter and less developed than the eastern end.

Just west, **Praia de Três Irmãos** is the slightly upscale beach cousin of Praia da Rocha. The eastern end of the beach is a beautiful cove, hemmed in by cliffs and ochre-coloured rocks. Beyond it, the beach stretches to **Alvor**, a classic Algarvian fishermen's village. Narrow cobbled streets plunge downhill to a quay and market where boats bob at anchor on a wide, marshy lagoon. A handful of bars rustle up barbecued sardines. At the top of the hill, on Rua da Igreja, is Igreja Matriz, a delightful 16th-century church, with a delicately carved Manueline portico, perhaps the finest on the Algarve, and excellent 18th-century *azulejos* in the chancel. A large white-sand beach is the main focus of a recreational area that includes a golf course and a casino.

Between Alvor and the N125, the main coastal road, are the **ruins of Abicada**, a Roman village that dates back to the 4th century AD.

Serra de Monchique

North of Portimão, and extending across the western half of the province, is the Serra de Monchique, a mountain range that protects the coast from the hot plains further north. The *serra* is a verdant landscape of cork, pine and chestnut trees and low-lying areas are covered in wildflowers. Its highest point is Fóia.

Two spots in the *serra* popular with visitors are the villages of Monchique and Caldas de Monchique. The first stop on the scenic journey along route N266 is the spa village of **Caldas de Monchique**, known since Roman times for its therapeutic waters. Its heyday was the Edwardian era, and many of the elegant buildings (including a casino and a

The Manueline Style

During the reign of Manuel I (1495–1521), artists were inspired as never before by the discovery of far-off lands and the romance of daring sea voyages. The style they evolved, called Manueline after their king, celebrated this brave new age of maritime travel. Motifs such as anchors, knotted ropes, sails, terrestrial globes, marine plants and animals became the signatures of this period's sculptors and architects. In the 16th century, the style fell out of favour and by 1540 Portugal had joined with the rest of Europe in building in the more sober Renaissance style.

The most famous example of Manueline art is Lisbon's Belém Tower, but you can also see exuberant stonework all over the Algarve. Look out for the church portals and windows at Silves (the Igreja da Misericórdia), Alvor, and particularly at Monchique.

handicrafts market) still date from this period. An air of nostalgia has long presided over this sleepy hollow, but a recent renovation programme has revitalised and widened its tourist appeal. The renovated hotels, restaurants and other facilities augment the more traditional shops.

Caldas de Monchique is a good place for a picnic and a stroll in the woods. The local waters are bottled and sold across the Algarve.

To the north of Caldas, the road starts to weave uphill quickly, rising some 300m (1,000ft) in 5km (3 miles) past terraced farmlands and forests of eucalyptus, oak

The famous Manueline portico of Monchique's Igreja Matriz

and cork. **Monchique** is a small market town, known for its handicrafts and the famous Manueline portico of its 16th-century **Igreja Matriz**. The beautiful, unusual church has Romanesque arches, stone columns, blue-and-yellow *azulejos* (tiles) and a handsome wood ceiling. If you wander around the town, you'll probably see artisans crafting shoes and carving out walking sticks in small workshops.

High above the town, the ruins of a 17th-century Franciscan monastery, **Nossa Senhora do Desterro**, loom like a ghostly grey eminence. Although the monastery itself is closed to the public, a visit here will be rewarded by a breathtaking view.

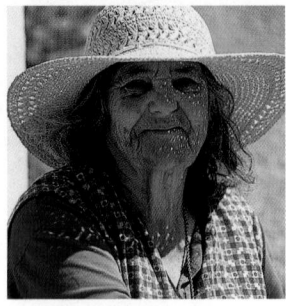

An old Algarvian

The road continues upwards, passing roadside souvenir stalls and fruit vendors and a few well-placed restaurants. At the end of the line is **Fóia**, almost 915m (3,000ft) above sea level, affording one of the best views in southern Portugal. There is no settlement here, just a collection of craft and souvenir stalls, a bar, a restaurant, TV masts and an obelisk marking the highest point on the Algarve. On a clear day you can see from the bay of Portimão to the Sagres peninsula and pick out the rocky outcrops of the Lagos beaches.

Although you may welcome the breeze after the heat of the coast, the wind blows pretty briskly at Fóia, so you'll need a jacket or sweater. Don't worry if you've forgotten to bring one; the best buys among the souvenirs here are chunky hand-knitted cardigans and pullovers.

Silves

Back down the main road towards Portimão, a turn-off to **Silves** leads to the former Moorish capital of the Algarve. More than eight centuries ago, Silves (then known as Chelb) was a magnificent city with palaces, gardens, bazaars and a huge red castle on a hill. Granada in Spain has the Alhambra, the legendary palace of the Moors, but the Algarve also possesses a city straight out of *Arabian Nights.*

The golden age of Silves began in AD711 with the Muslim invasion. With redoubtable fortifications and a population in the tens of thousands, it was one of the strongest outposts in 12th-century Arab Iberia. The Crusaders attacked and took the city in 1189, only to see it recovered by the Moors two years later. A half-decade later, the Christians captured Silves for good. However, the loss of Arabic wealth and the silting up of the River Arade left Silves almost literally high and dry, and by the time the bishopric of the Algarve was transferred to Faro in 1577, the town's population had dwindled to 140.

Its riches were stolen long ago, the once-great river is a silted shadow of its former self, and Silves is now just a dusty backwater, but the glorious setting remains. Surmounted by its red fortress, the white town climbs the hillside from the river, its medieval bridge still intact. The old city inside the gates still evokes the layout of the Jewish quarter and *almedina* of the Moors.

Though a castle of sorts has existed here since Phoenician times, the present **Castelo dos Mouros** (open daily 9am–6pm, until 6.30pm in summer; admission fee; tel: 282-445 624),

A view over Silves with the Old Cathedral in the distance

on the site of Roman or Visigothic foundations, took shape after the Christian Reconquest, though it preserves distinctly Moorish lines. Oleander and jacaranda soften its bellicose nature, and there are fine views over the tiled roofs of the town and surrounding countryside. A long-destroyed 'Palace of Verandas' once existed within the castle; today you can see only a deep well (60m/200ft).

Next to the castle is the impressive Gothic **Sé Velha** (Old Cathedral) of Silves, built by the liberating Crusaders, some of whom are buried within, in the 13th century. The remains of a Moorish mosque are hidden behind the altar. Opposite the Sé is the 16th-century **Igreja da Misericórdia**, with a classic Manueline-style side door.

Wander down to the main square, the Praça do Municipio. The imposing **Torreão da Porta da Cidade** (Turret of the City Gate) gives you a good idea of how seriously defence of the city was taken. This sturdy, war-like structure now houses the peaceful municipal library (open to the public). Close by, on Rua das Portas de Loulé, is a modern **Museu Municipal de Arqueologia** (archaeology museum). Here you can see part of a large Arab water cistern and other local finds.

Down by the river, the **Fábrica do Inglês** (English Factory; <www.fabrica-do-ingles.com>) is a leisure complex which was converted from a cork factory in 1999. Among its attractions are a cork museum, a variety of restaurants, bars and cafés, street entertainment and evening multimedia shows.

The hills around Silves form a prosperous farming region; figs, oranges, lemons, grapefruit, clementines and pomegranates are all grown in abundance in vast stretches of orchards.

Just outside the city, on the road to São Bartolomeu de Messines (route N124), is an important 16th-century religious sculpture. Known as the **Cruz de Portugal** (Cross of Portugal), it depicts the crucifixion of Christ on one face and the descent from the cross on the other.

If you are travelling by car, continue to the **Barragem** (dam) **do Arade**. The water collected in this reservoir surrounded by pine hills provides irrigation for the area's profitable orchards. It's perfect for a picnic as well as sailing and windsurfing.

East of Portimão

Lagoa, a sizeable town east of Portimão, is the province's wine capital. The acidic *vinhos da casa* served in most restaurants on the Algarve come from here. Lagoa wine, both red and white, is more powerful than ordinary wine, and the extra degree or two of alcoholic content can creep up on you. The local cooperative (Adega de Cooperativa de Lagoa; tel: 282-342 181) offers tours of the wineries and tastings, with 48 hours' notice.

From Lagoa, turn south about 5km (3 miles) to the charming resort of **Carvoeiro**, an archetypal small Barlavento

Fishing boats at Carvoeiro

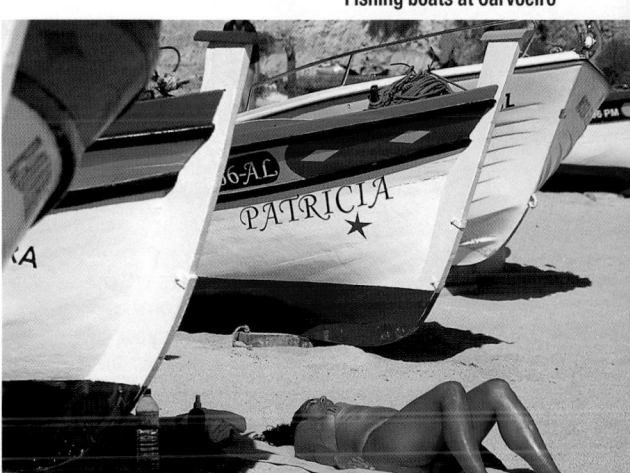

resort. The beach is the size of a tablecloth compared with some of the expanses to the east. A single road runs down through a pretty valley until it comes to a small crescent of sand shared by sunbathers and fishing boats. Above, rows of bright white houses perch on red sandstone cliffs, while cafés and restaurants fill the spaces in between. Carvoeiro is now fairly commercialised, but to many it remains one of the coast's most attractive resorts.

A narrow road follows the cliffs eastwards to the geological curiosity of **Algar Seco** ('dry gully'). Among other weird and wonderful shapes, wind and wave erosion have created a double-decker stone arch. There are walkways down to a lagoon enclosed by menacing rocks, and if weather conditions are calm, this open-air grotto is a paradise for snorkellers.

Algar Seco

Continue east and you will find three more beaches whose relative isolation has thus far protected them from development. They are (heading east) **Vale de Centianes**, **Praia do Carvalho** and **Praia de Benagil**. The last one in particular is superb, and is approached down a vertiginous road flanked by massive cliffs.

Back inland, just off the main road, is the attractive little village of **Porches**, with some classic, white Algarvian houses and filigreed chimneys. Porches is famous throughout Portugal for its hand-painted pottery, though you won't find much in the village itself. The shops of greatest renown are along the N125 route. Olaria Algarve (tel: 282-352 858), better known as Porches Pottery, is the biggest and best of these, with highly original designs and unique colours. Inside you can usually see a trio of women painting pieces. There's also an attractive little café-restaurant, itself decorated (of course)

Detail of an *azulejo* panel from the Casa Algarve

with wonderful ceramics. A little further east is Casa Algarve, which sells pottery and handicrafts in an attractive old house. More than others, it specialises in large-scale *azulejo* panels.

The coastal development nearby along the cliff tops continues apace. However, the vast majority of apartments and villas here are low-rise, and perhaps because the road system is not fully developed here, this part of the coast has largely escaped the attentions of mass tourism.

One of the most photographed beaches along this stretch is **Nossa Senhora da Rocha** (Our Lady of the Rock). The rock in question is a promontory, boldly jutting out into the sea, surmounted by a little white fishermen's church. On either side of the rock are two lovely half-moon coves, framed by cliffs.

The beach of **Armação de Pêra** is one of the longest in the Algarve – a flat, golden stretch to the east, picturesque rock stacks and small coves to the west. The massive development at the east end of town, though, has pretty much run roughshod over the natural beauty of the area, all but eclipsing the former fishing village. On the front, however, there is a pleasant esplanade and a small fortress, built in 1760 and home to a pretty chapel.

ALBUFEIRA AND CENTRAL ALGARVE

Albufeira

At one time a picturesque fishermen's town, **Albufeira** has grown wildly in recent years to become the leading resort in the Algarve. The area now generally referred to as Albufeira encompasses the coast from beyond Galé in the west all the way to Praia da Falésia, just before a marginally distinct resort area begins at Vilamoura. Parts of the commercial sprawl, while rarely grotesque, still overwhelm the little town at their centre.

Falésia Beach, situated to the east of Albufeira

Once you're off the traffic-squeezed main arteries, you will find that Albufeira's old town preserves a surprising amount of traditional charm. The cluster of whitewashed buildings includes a number of Moorish arches and three small churches.

Its magnificent setting – enormous, pockmarked sandstone cliffs rise above a huge beach lined with colourful fishing boats and hundreds of sunbathers – has proved resistant to development ruin. The gently sloping sands are perfect for family holidays, and if you are looking for a little more privacy you can escape the crowds by heading further east along the sandy coast. A tunnel links the centre of the town with the main beach.

When tractors haul the fishing fleet ashore, sunbathers jump from their towels to gape at the catch – 1m (3ft) eels, still flapping; large, spiny lobsters still snapping;

Albufeira's name evokes the town's Moorish roots. Indeed, the North African occupiers called it Al-Buhera ('castle on the sea'). Its cliff-top position and labyrinthine street plan provided an easily defensible spot for the Moors, and Albufeira proved one of the last towns to fall during the Reconquest. Its layout, however, did not save it from the 1755 earthquake, during which the town was almost completely destroyed.

and bucketloads of flat and silver fish. The famous beachside fish market buckled under logistics problems years ago and moved just north of the centre. It is still worth a visit, however, and you will also find fruit, vegetables and flowers on sale.

Modern Albufeira has fallen prey to mass tourism – international bars, cafés and nightspots pump out loud music day and night. There is little traditionally Portuguese about its raucous central square, but there are quiet spots to be found. And what brings all the tourists here, the Atlantic, is just a splash away. From almost any vantage point, the view of old Albufeira sloping up a gentle hill and its seascape is incredibly spectacular.

With so much activity to the east, the excellent beaches west of town are relatively uncrowded. The best are **São Rafael**, a beautiful, sandy strip with some splendidly shaped rocky outcrops, and **Coelha**, **Castelo** and **Galé**, three small, beautiful coves.

Hill Villages of Alte and Salir

One of the most picturesque settlements in the province is the lovely village of **Alte**, about 30km (18 miles) north of Albufeira. It is entered in romantic fashion, across a small, white bridge over a babbling stream that runs through town and waters a valley thick with oranges, pomegranates and figs.

The architectural highlight of the village is the 16th-century Igreja Matriz, entered through a classic Manueline portal. The church keeper will enthusiastically point out the many elaborate chapels and the rare 16th-century *azulejos* from Seville. The rest of Alte is the Algarve of postcards – white-washed houses along narrow streets, colourful windows, filigreed chimney pots and red-tiled roofs. And while their character may at first seem uniform, you won't see two houses the same.

Old boys relaxing in the shade in the picturesque village of Alte

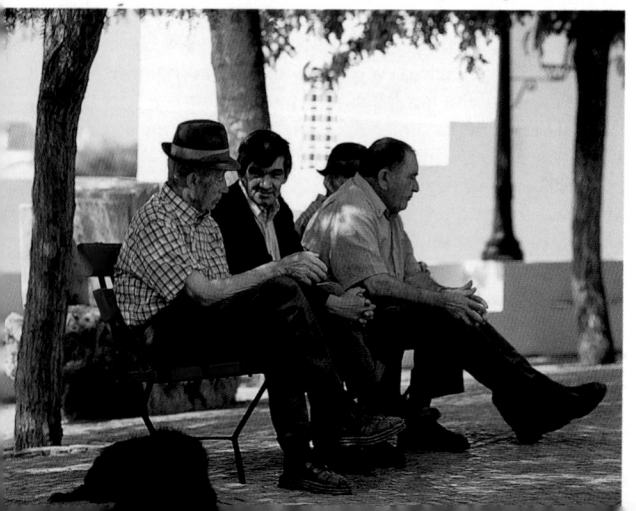

Follow the stream upriver and you come to the popular Fonte Pequena (Little Fountain) springs, where a restaurant and occasional folk dancing draw visitors. The setting is delightful and a perfect spot for a picnic.

If you continue east on the N124, you'll pass rolling hills and come to the pretty village of **Salir**, which is built on the edge of a steeply rising ridge and has two fine lookout points. The first is in the village itself, along-

Open any bottle of wine with a natural cork in it and the chances are the cork comes from Portugal. Over half the world's supply is produced here and you won't have to drive far in the Algarve to spot the cork oak. The tree is recognised by its broad, rounded head and glossy-green, holly-like leaves, or by the raw red trunk where the bark has been stripped off.

side the 16th-century parish church and water tower (don't miss the delightful gardens next door). The other, with the best views, is the adjacent peak, which once held a Moorish stronghold (follow signs to the *castelo*). All that remains of the castle are the bases of four huge turrets (12th–13th century) and some excavations. The old castle grounds are home to a tiny hamlet, complete with its own church. The panoramic views across to the main part of Salir and the surrounding countryside are spectacular, and there is even a tiny *miradouro* (belvedere) café here.

East from Albufeira

Loosely grouped with Albufeira are beaches to the east. Here, the coastline features the last of the dramatic rock formations that have made the Algarve so famous. At appealing **Olhos d'Agua**, a single road leads between pine-covered cliffs down to a soft, sandy beach shared by a gaily painted fishing fleet, eroded sandstone formations and sunbathers.

The resort derives its name from the 'eyes of water' that flow from strangely formed rocks, visible only at low tide.

Falésia is a beautiful beach framed by high cliffs, but to reach it you need to negotiate the grounds of the Sheraton Algarve hotel, whose lift down to the beach is for guests only. There are other excellent beaches at **Santa Eulalia** (longer and more open than Olhos de Agua), **Balaia**, **Praia da Oura** and **São João**. The latter two are regarded as satellites of Albufeira and may well be where you are staying on a package holiday to Albufeira. The centre of activity along this beach hinterland is the infamous 'strip' – a long street leading up to the hill-top area known as Montechoro. It's lined with a motley collection of bars, restaurants and nightspots.

Nearby **Vilamoura** is a wholly planned and sanitised community – Europe's largest 'from-scratch' private tourist

A line of yachts in Vilamoura's marina

undertaking. From high-rise hotels and sprawling villas that line manicured golf courses to the 19th-hole club bar and the Algarve's biggest marina, it is undeniably well done, but it could be anywhere. Still, it's a major draw for those who have their clubs ready for a golfing holiday; several of the Algarve's best courses have been sculpted out of the area.

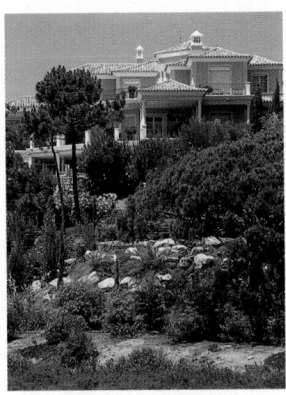

Luxury villa in Quinta do Lago

As new as everything looks and feels, the marina designers were not the first to take advantage of Vilamoura's harbour. The Romans built a dock in the same place and established an important fishing centre here. The Roman remains of **Cerro da Vila** were unearthed across the road from the marina. Aside from some low-level excavations showing the elaborate water-piping system and surviving mosaics and ceramics, there is also a small museum displaying everything from fishhooks to lamps, appealing to any student of archaeology.

A little further west, **Quarteira**, once a quiet fishing village, is today almost unrecognisable, subsumed under rows and rows of apartment buildings. The busy resort has a long, golden beach, and there are good, cheap restaurants in the old quarter where locals and adventurous visitors mingle. The municipal market still stands on the beach; every Wednesday one of the largest and busiest markets on the Algarve – offering fish and produce – is held next to it.

To the east of Vilamoura and Quarteira, the Algarvian terrain begins to change. The rugged, rocky lines of the

Barlavento coast west of Faro give way to the long, flat beaches of the east.

The small crossroads town of **Almancil** has shops, cafés and businesses, many of which are dedicated to serving British expatriates. But the town, of modest interest itself, is best known for what lies in its vicinity. Many of these expats live a few kilometres south on the coast, and it is here that two of the Algarve's most luxurious and exclusive resorts are found.

Each is reached down long roads that become progressively more private-looking as the beach nears. **Vale do Lobo** means 'Valley of the Wolf', but it could just as well mean 'Valley of the Dolls'; it is a security-conscious, maze-like villa community concealed behind a giant entrance gate. Guards do their best to keep the beach the domain of the expatriate and wealthy tourist classes. **Quinta do Lago**, a few kilometres down the coast, refers to the hotel of the same name, once owned by Prince Faisal of Saudi Arabia, and the luxury homes that have sprouted up around it. Quinta do Lago has two of the finest golf courses on the Algarve and has regularly hosted the Portuguese Open. The beach is reached across a long, nostalgic wooden bridge that crosses wetlands and bird sanctuaries of the **Ria Formosa Nature Reserve**. On the beach is a terrific, if expensive, restaurant for fresh-caught fish, which you pick out and have grilled.

Ria Formosa Nature Reserve

São Lourenço dos Matos

Back towards Almancil is one of the Algarve's top attractions, but if you're not looking closely, it's easy to miss. About 16km (10 miles) west of Faro, a simple white church stands out on a small hill overlooking the thundering highway. A sign simply says 'S. Lourenço' – indicating the turn-off to **São Lourenço dos Matos** (Church of St Lawrence of the Woods; open Tues–Sat 10am–1pm and 2.30–6pm, until 5pm in winter, Mon 2.30–5pm only; admission fee; tel: 289-395 451). Inside is one of the most extraordinary displays of *azulejo* design you'll ever see. Every square centimetre of the baroque, 15th-century church – its walls, vaulted ceiling and cupola – is covered with hand-painted, blue-and-white

São Lourenço dos Matos

ceramic tiles. Most date from the early 18th century and depict biblical scenes detailing the life of St Lawrence, born across the border in Huesca, Spain. The only element of the church not blue-and-white is the carved, gilded altar. The ensemble is a stunning sight, not to be missed. Worth visiting too is the nearby **São Lourenço Cultural Centre**, which hosts modern art exhibitions and concerts, and has a delightful sculpture garden.

Loulé

North of Almancil, **Loulé** is a regional produce centre with a large Saturday market, known for its leather, lace and copper goods. Loulé is a prosperous town with an ambitious, modern boulevard complete with outdoor cafés that are jam-packed on market day. Coach parties come from far and wide to shop at the colourful, bustling market.

There are actually two markets. Fresh produce, including fish, is sold in a mock-Moorish hall, while a 'Gypsy market' is held towards the opposite end of the boulevard. Just below the permanent market halls, on the main Praça da República, you'll find a well-preserved section of the medieval castle walls (which were much damaged by the 1755 earthquake). The ramparts afford excellent views from the town, and set into the castle remains is a modest local museum. Also worth visiting are the **Igreja Matriz** (São Clemente), a 13th-century Gothic church with 18th-century *azulejos* (tiles); the **Convento da Graça**, with a terrific Manueline portal; and **Ermida de Nossa Senhora da Conceição**, a small church prized for its baroque altar and ceramic tiles.

In the streets directly below the castle walls, you may well hear the sounds of craftsmen beating copper – from whom you can buy direct. You can also see artisans at work on the pottery wheel, producing leather goods (such as

---

Filigreed Flues

Tourism has often been called an industry without chimneys, but not so in the Algarve, where smokestacks – graceful, lattice creations, reminiscent of Moorish lanterns – have become a trademark of the region. For hundreds of years, Algarve homeowners have taken great pride in the beauty and originality of their chimneys. The popular dictum is the more elaborate the chimney pot, the wealthier the owner. Originally carved of wood, later ceramic, and then eventually concrete was used. The area around Faro and Olhão in particular enjoy a strong reputation for rooftop art, but keep your eyes skyward and you'll see pretty chimney pots all over the Algarve.

decorated saddles and bridles) and furniture. The craftsmen of Loulé are said to be the descendants of a community of Muslims who found refuge in the district at the end of the Christian Reconquest. If you are in the Algarve in springtime, don't miss the Loulé Carnival. The parades, 'Battle of Flowers' and musical celebrations are the best of their kind in the region.

The flower-lined road from Loulé to **São Brás de Alportel**, another market

A family of storks takes advantage of an Algarvian chimney

town and site of one of only two *pousadas* (government-owned inns) along the Algarve, passes through rolling orchards of fig, olive and orange trees. It's best to visit the town on Saturday, when the lively market transforms its otherwise sleepy character. You may wish to pay a visit to the lovely **Museu Regional do Algarve** (Ethnographic Museum), where exhibits of Algarvian costumes are well staged in a large, old house 90m (100yds) or so off the main square.

In this northern part of the province, life is visibly slower and more rustic; bonneted ladies in black walk along the roadside, old men are carried aloft donkeys, and families pluck almonds from the trees with long sticks.

Towards Faro

On the road towards Faro is a pair of historical sights. The **Palácio de Estói** (currently closed to the public) is a most curious find. The charming rococo palace, found through a small side gate just to the left of the church steps in the town centre, once belonged to the Dukes of Estói. Begun during the mid-18th century, in palatial terms, it's rather small, abandoned and visibly dilapidated; however, it is soon to be transformed into a new *pousada* (a state-owned hotel, usually – as here – housed within an historic building) and should be one of the most interesting *pousadas* in which visitors can stay. Even prior to the conversion, it is a spectacular sight. Its faded glory includes balustrade terraces and staircases with splendid bursts of bougainvillea, busts of historic characters impaled on the parapets, brightly coloured wall tiles and formal gardens.

The dusty **Villa Romana de Milreu** (Roman ruins of Milreu) is located 1.5km (1 mile) down the road from the village, on the route towards Faro (a small sign on the side of the road reads 'Ruinas de Milreu'). Some 1,400 years before the Palace of Estói was erected, Milreu was also the large country house of an eminent person. The knee-high walls that trace the outline of this once-luxurious establishment are still clearly visible. The tall, semi-circular tower ruin is thought to have been a temple to pagan water gods at one time; however, by the 5th century it had clearly been converted to a church.

FARO AND ENVIRONS

Faro, the provincial capital of the Algarve, is also the one that seems to get the least respect from tourists. Many fly into Faro, make a beeline for their resorts and return two weeks later, bypassing the city for the airport. Those who take the time – a day is sufficient – to explore Faro find an atmosphere quite distinct from the resort-heavy coast. Faro has a greater wealth of cultural and historic monuments than any other Algarvian town, a picturesque old quarter and best of all, tourists never overrun authentic Portuguese restaurants, cafés and bars.

A view across Faro's harbour with the Arco da Vila to the right

Faro was always an important town, even during Roman times, when it was allowed to mint its own coins. It continued to thrive under the Arabs; its name may be derived from the name *Harune,* one of the old city's ruling families. The Christians recaptured Faro in 1249, completing the Reconquest, and the city prospered, becoming the episcopal see of the Bishop of the Algarve in 1577. But in 1596, when it was Spanish territory, an English fleet commanded by Queen Elizabeth I's favourite, the Earl of Essex, sacked and burned the capital.

Until comparatively recently, when the area silted into a tidal flat, Faro was a commercial and fishing port open to the Atlantic. Indeed, the Earl of Essex's fleet had sailed right up to the city's Arab fortifications. Today, small fishing boats and pleasure craft must zigzag carefully amid the dunes and then creep beneath the railway bridge to enter the sleepy harbour.

Old Town

The main entrance to the circular old town, near the harbour, is the 19th-century **Arco da Vila**, a lovely arch and bell tower habitually crowned by a venerable family of nesting storks. Beyond the arch, a cobbled street, worn slick by centuries of tramping feet, leads up to the splendid expanse of the **Largo da Sé** (Cathedral Square), best seen in the evening when floodlit and free of cars.

The only remains of the 13th-century Gothic **Sé** (open Mon–Fri 10am–noon and 2–5pm; admission fee for museum and tower) are

The cathedral tower

the unusual cathedral tower, main portico and two interior chapels. The entrance is at the side. As you enter, look out for the remains of the Capela dos Ossos (Bone Chapel). Inside are some fine examples of *azulejos* and superb statues and carvings, one of the Algarve's top collections of 17th- and 18th-century religious art. Climb the tower for fine views over the whole of Faro.

Across the square is the **Paço Episcopal** (Bishop's Palace), an excellent example of the plain *chã* style prevalent during the 17th century. To its right is the *Câmara Municipal* (Town Hall).

➤ The **Convento de Nossa Senhora da Assunção** (Convent of Our Lady of the Assumption) contains the most beautiful cloister in southern Portugal. The first Renaissance building in the Algarve, it was constructed in the 16th century on the site of the old Jewish quarter (Faro had a sizeable Jewish population in the Middle Ages). Abandoned as a convent in the 19th century and then put to use as a cork factory, it has been beautifully restored as a museum devoted to archaeology, the **Museu Arqueológico Infante Dom Henrique** ◀ (open Tues–Fri 10am–6pm, Sat and Sun 2–6pm; until 5.30pm winter; admission fee; tel: 289-822 042). The principal exhibit is a 2,000-year-old Roman floor mosaic measuring 9m (30ft) long and 3m (10ft) wide. Unearthed in Faro, it is nicknamed the 'Ocean Mosaic', for it depicts a bearded sea-god (though the bulldozer that discovered it in 1976 shaved off the lower half of his face). There are also busts taken from the Roman ruins at Milreu. Displays of Portuguese art are housed in the many rooms off the cloister.

Nearby is the **Ermida de Nossa Senhora do Repouso** (Hermitage of Our Lady of Rest), a tiny 18th-century chapel carved out of the ancient Moorish arches.

Just outside the old quarter is the **Igreja de São Francisco** (Church of St Francis), which was begun in the late 17th century. Narrative tiles adorn the main chapel and vaulted ceiling, which displays a terrific panel of the Coronation of the Virgin Mary.

Town Centre

In the centre of town, across from the harbour, the cobbled and shaded municipal **Jardim Manuel Bívar**, created in the 15th century as Queen's Square, is a popular meeting place for young and

> The real attraction of Faro's old town is not its set-piece buildings, but the quiet, hidden, timeless flavour of its tiny houses and narrow, cobbled alleyways. A good place to sit and absorb some of it is the Café do Largo, where classical music accompanies your coffee.

old alike. In its centre are an open-air café and an old-fashioned bandstand. Several handsome 16th- to 18th-century mansions surround the square, including the Banco de Portugal building and the Palácio Belmarço.

As in several other Algarve towns, the main shopping area of central Faro is pedestrian-only, and cafés and restaurants spill out onto the street, fish displays and all. Rua de Santo António is the main thoroughfare. At its far end is the **Museu Regional do Algarve** (Ethnographic Museum), with displays of local handicrafts, reconstructions of rooms in a typical Algarvian house, and a colourful watercart that Manuel Ignacio Miguel of Olhão operated for 60 years, almost up to his death in 1974. The museum sits on the edge of Faro's Mouraria, or old Moorish quarter. It's worth wandering the streets that lead to **Largo do Pé da Cruz** and the attractive little 17th-century chapel of the same name (Our Lady of the Foot of the Cross).

The chilling interior of the Capela dos Ossos in the Igreja do Carmo

The new town, an expansion dating from the 19th century, is west of here. Two churches, which face each other across the large and congested Largo do Carmo, are worth seeing. The **Igreja de São Pedro** (Church of St Peter) is the smaller of the two, built in the 16th century. It has a carved baroque retable and a couple of rococo chapels.

But Faro's finest church is **Igreja do Carmo** (Carmelite Church; open Mon–Fri 10am–1pm and 3–5pm, Sat morning only; admission fee; tel: 289-824 490), which took most of the 18th century to build. The twin bell towers and stately façade are matched by a beautiful gilded interior, but the greatest attraction is the macabre **Capela dos Ossos** (Chapel of Bones). This 19th-century curiosity, like a similar chapel in the town of Évora further north, is constructed of the skulls and bones of monks, unearthed from the friars' cemetery. Depending on your tolerance for such things, it is either fascinating or sick beyond belief.

Less ghastly is the **Jewish Cemetery**, on the outskirts of town (off Rua Leão Penedo, near Praça dos Bomberos de Faro). Dating to the early 19th century, it has more than 100 tombstones in Hebrew, testimony to the once-important Jewish community in Faro.

Few people seem to do it, but it is well worth spending a night or two in Faro, especially if you've already spent some time in a traditional Algarvian beach resort. Watch the sun setting over the fishing boats in the lagoon while you have a drink in the splendidly old-fashioned, cavernous Café Aliança, the city's oldest café. Faro also has some lively music bars.

Praia de Faro

Faro's beach, the **Praia de Faro**, is noted for its water sports. You can drive there across the single-lane causeway linking the long strip of dunes with the mainland (no buses or motor

Sunset over Faro's lagoon

homes allowed), or in the summer catch a ferry from the pier by the old town. If the sea is rough, simply cross to the opposite side of the sand spit and swim in the calm, warmer waters of the lagoon (though be aware, it can sometimes be muddy and a little unpleasant).

EASTERN ALGARVE

Olhão

Heading east from Faro, the first settlement of any size you will come to is the fishing town of **Olhão**. A working port, it has made few concessions to tourism and is full of character.

Olhão has often been described as the 'little white Cubist town of the Algarve', its architecture likened to that of North African towns. That may have been the case some years ago, but modern development has strongly interfered with its once-distinctive appearance. You can judge for yourself by ascending the bell tower of the parish church, **Nossa Senhora do Rosário**, which you'll find by winding your way through the narrow streets back to the Praça da Restauração (you may have to ask for access to the tower in the sacristy). Founded by King Dom Pedro II in 1698, the church has an impressive, scroll-decorated baroque façade, brilliant white dome, stone bell tower and a chapel at the rear, **Nossa Senhora dos Aflitos** (Our Lady of the

Afflicted), where women often pray when their fishermen husbands are away at sea.

Instead of the red-tiled roofs and filigreed chimneys seen elsewhere in the Algarve, the Olhão skyline comprises flat-topped roofs of terraces called *açoeitas*. Look carefully and you can still see the narrow, outside staircases leading to white-washed towers, where fishermen's wives, or perhaps smugglers, would look out for the incoming fleet.

The name of the square, **Praça da Restauração** ('Restoration Square'), recalls Olhão's most glorious moment, when an improvised local army rebelled against Napoleon's occupying forces in 1808. This insurrectionary zeal subsequently spread throughout the rest of Portugal and resulted in Olhão being awarded the title 'Noble Town of the Restoration'.

Olhão's fishing port is worth a look. The fishermen of the town have a reputation for hardiness – some used to earn a living in the cod-stocked waters as far away as Newfoundland. During the past two centuries, however, some of the sailors have turned away from fishing and instead, taken to the cargo trade between Portugal and North Africa. This relatively recent link with the neighbouring continent may have been the inspiration for the local North African style of architecture. In any case, it developed long after the Moors had left the Algarve.

Nossa Senhora dos Aflitos

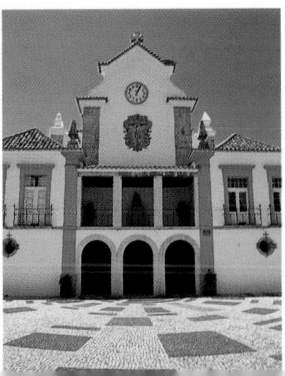

You're unlikely to see a boat coming in from another continent, but you are guaranteed the hustle, bustle, sights, smells and sounds of one at the **Olhão fish market**, one of the Algarve's best (the town is especially famous for its mussels and other shellfish). Adjacent to the voluminous market buildings are small, well-tended parks, one of which boasts several splendid benches decorated with blue-and-white *azulejos*. Just beyond the park on the other side, ferries depart regularly in summer for the barrier-island beaches of **Armona** and **Culatra** just offshore. These lovely, under-developed beaches are the jewels of the coastline between Faro and Tavira.

A little further along the coast, at **Fuzeta**, is another popular beach. There is some holiday development here, but as yet only on a small scale. Fuzeta itself is little more than a few gaily painted boats bobbing at anchor on the inlet, while in the background local workers rake salt crystals into small white mountains punctuating the delta.

Turn inland, because the small village of **Moncarapacho**, with a fine old church, a sleepy village square and a fascinating little museum, is well worth the 8-km (5-mile) detour. The countryside around here is full of orange and almond groves and, as you head east (back on the main

Azulejos

It is thanks to the Moors that Portugal is so liberally endowed with glazed tiles, or *azulejos*. The name probably derives from the Arabic *Al Zulaicha*, or *Zuleija*, meaning ceramic mosaic. Other influences were painters from France, Italy and Germany, as well as Portugal's maritime empire.

Mass production began after the 1755 earthquake, but small family businesses using old methods continued, and still exist today. A fine example of the craft is in the church of São Lourenço in Almansil. Its interior walls and dome are entirely faced with blue-and-white tiles depicting scenes from the life of St Lawrence. Other examples are the tiled stairways in the gardens of the villa at Estói and the scenes from the life of St Francis in the Church of São Francisco in Faro.

This *azulejo* in Olhão reflects the town's principal trade

road) towards Tavira, olive groves and vineyards also start to appear. Tavira's grapes produce a good, rustic wine consumed all over the Algarve.

Tavira

After the salty flavour of Olhão and the rural serenity of Moncarapacho, the aristocratic bearings of **Tavira**, one of the true gems of the Algarve, may come as something of a surprise. One of the region's most historic cities, its Moorish, *Reconquista* and Renaissance roots are clearly visible.

In the 1500s, Tavira had the largest population on the Algarve. This tuna-fishing port and self-assured town of historic churches, imposing classical-style mansions and riverfront gardens probably dates back as far as the Phoenicians or the Carthaginians. Its seven-arched stone bridge of Roman origin is still in use. Tavira's **castle** (open Mon–Fri 9am–5pm, weekends and holidays 10am–5pm), in the middle of the *centro histórico* (old quarter), was a defensive structure built by the Moors. Climb the walls for a superb panoramic view of the city, but be careful, as the ramparts have no hand-rails. Within the walls is an attractive, fragrant garden.

The walls look directly onto the **Igreja de Santa Maria do Castelo** (Church of St Mary of the Castle), most likely built on the site of the old mosque. The Gothic portal is the only original 13th-century part of the building to have survived the devastating 1755 earthquake. In the chancel is the large tomb of Dom Paio Peres Correia, who drove the Moors out of Tavira in 1242.

Across the square, the ochre-coloured former convent, **Convento da Graça**, is being converted into a *pousada* (inn) by the Portuguese Government and is due to open in early 2006.

Just down the hill, off Rua Galeria near the river, is the beautiful 16th-century **Igreja da Misericórdia** (Church of

The historic city of Tavira on the banks of the Gilão

Mercy), a spectacular Renaissance edifice. The carved portico is especially fine, with a statue of Our Lady of Mercy under a canopy. The 18th-century interior contains fine gilded woodwork and *azulejos*.

Rua da Liberdade, Tavira's main street, is lined with stately 16th-century mansions. A walk down any of the city's old streets will reveal handsome details of

An elegant façade along Tavira's Rua da Liberdade

noble houses, such as double windows and latticed doors. A lively fruit and vegetable market is held by the banks of the River Gilão, and it is well worth crossing the Roman bridge to view more of the town's elegant houses and pretty flower-filled squares. Many of those houses have sloping triangular roofs, called *tesouros* (treasures).

Around Tavira

A nice excursion from Tavira is to the nearby island **Ilha de Tavira**, where there is a huge and thoroughly appealing beach backed by sand dunes. Boats leave from Quatro Águas, 2km (1 mile) east of town.

Back on the mainland, a turn-off from the main road east of Tavira leads to a perfectly enchanting little whitewashed village overlooking the sea. Pretty **Cacela Velha** can't have more than 100 inhabitants. It has an 18th-century church, a telephone booth, a cemetery, an old well and a handful of well-tended, blue-and-white houses festooned with flowers.

East of here lies the fledgling resort of **Manta Rota**, a former fishing village, and the high-rise canyons of **Monte**

Cemetery at Cacela Velha

Gordo. The reason behind all this development is a long sandy beach, which stretches undisturbed for some 10km (6 miles) between the two resorts and is backed by pine trees and dunes. Although the last in a long line of Algarve beach resorts (or the first, if you're coming from Spain) is not, by a long shot, the coast's most attractive, the beach and water-sports facilities at Monte Gordo are enough to attract and entertain many serious sun-seekers. By night the casino is the focus of attention.

Castro Marim

The Guadiana River, which runs into the Atlantic 3km (2 miles) east of Monte Gordo, served as a natural frontier for 2,000 years, forming the boundary between the Roman provinces of Lusitania (Portugal) and Baetica (southern Spain). This explains the strategic importance of **Castro Marim**, a former fortress town rising from the flatlands to command the broad river. For five centuries its primitive castle-fortress was occupied by the Moors. After the Christian Reconquest it became the home of the new Military Order of Christ (succeeding the disbanded Knights Templars).

Below the castle, the saltpans and unpolluted marshlands of the local nature reserve attract a large number of waders (look out for storks, egrets and black-winged stilts). In 1991 a new suspension bridge across the river was built to link southern Portugal and southern Spain, and the formal border between the two countries has since been abolished.

It is worth driving north along the Guadiana for the pretty scenery and riverside villages. Timeless **Alcoutim** is crowned by castle ruins and looks across at Sanlúcar in Spain, similarly dominated by ancient fortress remains. A ferry links the two villages and boats are available for river trips.

In the remote hills to the southwest, the **Parque Miniero Cova dos Mouros** (2km/1 mile south of Vaqueiros) is a reconstruction of an Iron Age mining settlement. The copper mines here were used for over 5,000 years; you can still see mine shafts, along with rebuilt huts, a fort and furnaces. Other attractions of this ecological park are the rides on Iberian donkeys, natural pools for swimming and marked footpaths for exploring the flora and fauna of the unspoilt countryside.

Vila Real de Santo António

Vila Real de Santo António

Returning to the coast, the town of **Vila Real de Santo António** (the Royal Town of St Anthony) is the last of the Algarve's beach towns before Spain. The city was designed to be as grand as its name suggests, in order to impress the Spanish on the other side of the river. The town plan was the inspiration of the Marquês of Pombal, King José I's favoured architect, and the town was built in just five months in 1774, aping the grid layout of Lisbon's Baixa (lower city).

The town square, the **Praça do Marquês do Pombal**, is the work of the royal architect and the tour de force of Vila Real. The pavement's black-and-white wedges of stone radiate from an obelisk in the centre of the square like rays from the sun. Distinguished three-storey, late 18th-century houses line the square, and orange trees soften the edges, adding colour and scent. Visit the small **Manuel Cabanas Museum**, just off the square, to see a nice collection of woodcuts that ranges from rustic scenes to famous statesmen and composers.

Today Vila Real is quiet but dignified. A walk around the old quarter reveals a number of fine, brightly painted houses along pedestrian-only streets. Vila Real de Santo António's main appeal is as the ferry port to **Ayamonte** across the water in Spain. The trip takes just 20 minutes – less time than it would take to drive to and over the new bridge – and the white town of Ayamonte is a fine sight as you approach it from the river.

EXCURSION TO LISBON

Until the 19th century, the overland journey from the Algarve to Lisbon, Portugal's capital city, took a week or more. Now it's only a few hours by road or rail, and you can fly from Faro in just 40 minutes.

For years Lisbon has had a reputation as a relatively quiet, easy-going town, lacking the hustle and bustle of other major European cities. But while this is still true to a degree, the gap is closing and Lisbon is becoming altogether more European.

The centre of Lisbon is small, compact and easy to get around in just a couple of days. Moreover, it has two lovely old quarters that are as full of character as any place in Europe.

The city is built on hills – by legend seven, in fact many more – but the great thing for the visitor is the splendid vantage points and lookouts that these provide. The best place to start your tour of Lisbon is from the Moors' old castle, the **Castelo de São Jorge**, the king of all vantage points. From here you can look out over the whole of the city and along the broad Rio Tejo (River Tagus), spanned by one of the longest suspension bridges in Europe.

The castle is set just above Lisbon's most famous *bairro* (district), the **Alfama**. Here you will discover a labyrinth of narrow, crooked streets, cobbled alleyways, decaying old houses, former palaces, fish stalls and bars totally unknown to the vast majority of tourists. Little has changed here in decades, if not centuries.

Another majestic view of the city is from the **Miradouro de Santa Luzia**, a park just down the hill from the castle. Nearby is the **Sé** (Cathedral), which has an ancient, cavernous interior – one of perhaps a dozen first-class churches in the city. Adjacent to the cathedral is the **Igreja de Santo António da Sé**, named for the patron saint of Lisbon, St Anthony of Padua.

A view across the city to the Castelo de São Jorge

Just beyond the dense quarters of the Alfama is **São Vicente de Fora** (St Vincent Beyond the Walls), an Italianate church and monastic cloister. The latter is the true highlight: its walls and courtyards are lined with blue-and-white *azulejos*, and the views from the roof are among the best in the city.

Down towards the river is the **Museu Nacional do**

Elevador de Santa Justa

Azulejo (National Tile Museum), devoted entirely to the art of painted and glazed ceramic tiles, a national art form. About 12,000 *azulejos* are on show here, from 15th-century polychrome designs to 20th-century Art Deco. A prized possession is the *Lisbon Panorama*, a 36m- (118ft-) long tile composition of Lisbon's riverside as it looked before the Great Earthquake of 1755.

The **Bairro Alto** (upper city) is a hilly area full of evocative houses decorated with wrought-iron balconies usually occupied by birdcages and flowerpots. At night the district is loaded with an exciting atmosphere and is famous for its *fado* (folk music) clubs. It's a relatively harmless place by day, but you should be on your guard if visiting after dark.

Perched on the edge of the Bairro Alto is the **Igreja do Carmo**, a convent devastated in the earthquake of 1755 but deliberately preserved as an atmospheric ruin and potent reminder of its impact. Nearby, the sumptuous, 16th-century **Igreja de São Roque** features a small museum of sacred art.

The convent used to be connected to the lower city by the landmark 30m (98ft) **Elevador de Santa Justa**, a lift situated off the Rossio square in the Baixa; however, the walkway linking the lift and the upper city was destroyed in a fire that swept through Lisbon in 1988, and nowadays you can only go to the top of the Elevador (definitely worth the effort for the excellent views). This 1902 Victorian marvel of iron and glass was built by Raul Mesnier, not, as popularly believed, by Gustave Eiffel. To reach the upmarket shopping area of **Chiado**, now totally rebuilt after the 1988 fire, you have to slowly meander up behind the Elevador.

The **Baixa** is Lisbon's principal business district. The main square is the **Praça Dom Pedro IV**, better known as **Rossio**. Look out for the railway station, **Estação do Rossio**, which looks like a Moorish palace with horseshoe arches, just west of the square. Two blocks north is another lively square, **Praça dos Restauradores**, which leads to the leafy main thoroughfare, Avenida da Liberdade.

The city plunges steeply downhill to the River Tagus and its most imposing square, **Praça do Comércio**, lined on three sides by gracious arcaded buildings and a vast triumphal arch. The grand square, wholly wiped out by the earthquake of 1755, has seen its share of watershed political events: King Carlos and his son were felled by assassins'

A fountain on Lisbon's main square, the Rossio

bullets in the square in 1908, and one of the first uprisings of the Carnation Revolution of 1974 was staged here.

Moving west and down towards the river from Praça do Comércio is the elegant residential neighbourhood called Lapa. Its standout sight is the **Museu Nacional de Arte Antiga** (National Museum of Ancient Art), Portugal's largest museum. Among its pieces of international renown are *The Adoration of St Vincent,* a multi-panel work attributed to the 15th-century Portuguese master, Nuno Gonçalves; and *The Temptation of St Anthony*, a fantastic hallucination by Hieronymus Bosch, tempered with humour and executed with mad genius.

Some 6km (4 miles) west of Praça do Comércio is the riverside district of **Belém**. It was from here that the Age of Exploration (begun on the Algarve) reached its zenith between 1497 and 1499, when Vasco da Gama's voyage to India opened up a major new sea route. During the following century, Portugal enjoyed a golden age of trade, and King Manuel celebrated the discoverers with two magnificent monuments.

The most famous is the diminutive but exquisitely formed Torre de Belém. By contrast the majestic **Mosteiro dos Jerónimos** is Lisbon's largest religious monument and a formidable example of Manueline architecture. The church and its double-decker cloister survived the 1755 earthquake; in addition to housing royal tombs it also holds the relics of national heroes Vasco da Gama and the poet Luis de Camões. The monastery houses an archaeology museum, and next door is the **Museu da Marinha** (Naval Museum). Back down the street towards the town centre is the **Museu Nacional dos Coches** (National Coach Museum), housed in the former riding school of the Belém Royal Palace.

Also in Belém is the modern **Padrão dos Descobrimentos** (Monument to the Discoverers). This huge waterfront sculpture depicts Prince Henry the Navigator at the prow of

Padrão dos Descobrimentos

a stylised caravel that juts into the Tagus. The figures behind represent noted explorers, map-makers and astronomers whom Prince Henry mobilised in order to launch Portuguese ships into the history books.

Opposite the Padrão is the stylish **Centro Cultural de Belém**, which puts on temporary exhibitions and concerts and is also home to Lisbon's Design Museum. The restaurant here has fine views over the river and the Padráo dos Descobrimentos.

One of Lisbon's newest attraction is the park designed for Expo '98, which did much to reinvigorate the industrial eastern section of the city. The riverfront **Parque das Nações** (Nations Park) continues to draw visitors with the largest aquarium in Europe (**Oceanário de Lisboa**), an interactive science museum and cable cars up to Torre de Vasco da Gama, the highest point in the city. The park is easily accessible by Metro.

WHAT TO DO

SPORTS

The Algarve is a top destination for sports holidays. With great weather and superbly designed courses, the region has long been famous for golf. Tennis is also big, and some former big names in British tennis have taken advantage of the favourable climate to set up schools here. And with around 160km (100 miles) of south-facing beaches, there is plenty of scope for water-sports enthusiasts.

Golf

Although a year-round sport on the Algarve, golf is played mainly from October to May. There are 27 major golf courses, many designed by the sport's biggest names. All boast luxury clubhouses, manicured greens and immaculate fairways. The top courses are to be found around Vilamoura and stretch west to Lagos. Green fees range from €60 to €200 (discounts possible) for 18 holes. All courses are open to visitors; most require an official handicap certificate and proper dress. The best are:

Palmares (near Lagos): 18 holes. A challenging course with an ocean panorama, plus high hills and deep valleys. Views of Bay of Lagos. Tel: 282-762 961.

Parque da Floresta (Budens, near Salema): 18 holes. A spectacular rolling hillside course offering excellent value. A favourite with families, offering a wide range of sporting facilities, a heated outdoor pool and a health and beauty spa. Tel: 282-690 054.

Penina (near Portimão): 36 holes. The longest and oldest course, with a distinguished championship history. Waterways and lakes are a dominant feature. Championship course, re-

The famous 16th hole at Vale do Lobo's Royal Golf Course

Algarve Golf can arrange discount rates and various packages and will provide vouchers to be collected at Faro airport. There are packages for playing all the courses at Vilamoura – 5 rounds in 7 days, €285 (high season); 7 rounds in 10 days, €395; <www.algarvegolf.net>

quired handicap 28 men, 32 women. Tel: 282-420 200.

Quinta do Lago: Two 18-hole courses, Quinta do Lago south and Quinta do Lago north. Among Europe's finest courses. American-designed with outstanding lush greens and roomy fairways. Tel: 289-390 700.

Royal (Vale do Lobo): 18 holes. A rugged terrain with fine views. The 16th hole is 'the most photographed hole in Europe'. Tel: 289-396 522.

San Lorenzo (near Quinta do Lago): 18 holes. Ranked by Golf World as the 5th-best course in Europe. Required handicap, 28 men, 36 women. Tel: 289-396 522.

Sheraton Pine Cliffs (Praia Falésia): 9 holes. Although not the most challenging of the Algarve's courses, it's certainly one of the most picturesque, with a clifftop layout overlooking the sea. Tel: 289-500 100.

Vilamoura: For all Vilamoura courses, reserve at least two days ahead by calling central reservations. Tel: 289-310 333.

Vilamoura Laguna: 18 holes. Designed by Joseph Lee, opened in 1993. Known for its water hazards. Tel: 289-310 180.

Vilamoura Millennium: 18 holes. Designed by Martin Hawtree and opened in May 2000. Beautifully integrated into the environmental park at Vilamoura. Tel: 289-310 188.

Vilamoura Old Course: 18 holes. Designed by Frank Pennink, this is a classic English-style course. Golfers must present a certificate of handicap no greater than 24 (men) or 28 (women). Tel: 289-310 341.

Vilamoura Pinhal: 18 holes. Originally designed by Frank Pennink and renovated by the American architect

Robert Trent Jones in 1985. First 9 holes are among the pines, the last 9 have views of the sea. Tel: 289-310 390.

Vilamoura Victoria: 18 holes. The newest of the swanky courses at Vilamoura and the longest golf course in Portugal. Designed by Arnold Palmer. Tel: 289-320 500.

Vilamoura Vila Sol: 18 holes. Considered to have among the best fairways in the Algarve. Tel: 289-300 505.

For details of all the courses visit <www.algarvegolf.net> or pick up a copy of the golfing brochure *Algarve – Land of Golf*, with information on all of the courses. Keen golfers should consider the option of accommodation at a hotel affiliated with a golf course. Typically these are establishments very close to the top golf courses that offer free (or discounted) golf on courses that may otherwise be hard to get a game on. They also arrange tournaments among their guests. Staying at a villa on the fringes of a fairway is another means of securing green-fee discounts and guaranteeing preferential tee times.

Surfing at Beliche Beach

Water Sports

Most of the larger beaches have equipment for hire, but don't count on expert tuition everywhere. Aside from the main beach resorts, there are good facilities at Praia da Luz (where the Ocean Club has its own water-sports centre), the marina at Vilam-

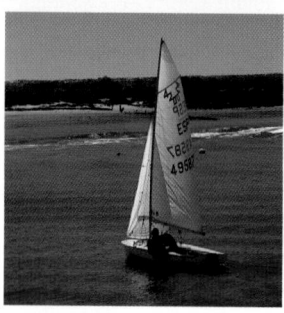

Plain sailing

oura, Quinta do Lago, Praia da Martinhal and Sagres.

Jet-skiing. For more high-speed fun on the water you can rent a jet-ski at Praia da Rocha, Quarteira, Alvor or Quinta do Lago.

Sailing. Dinghies and instruction are available at Praia de Luz, Quinta do Lago and Portimão. Sailing is also possible on the dam, Barragem do Arade. For bigger craft try the marina at Vilamoura or the Carvoeiro Club. Anchorage and harbour facilities are available at Lagos, Faro, Olhão, Portimão, Sagres and Vila Real. Boat cruises are available in nearly all spots along the Algarve. **Bom Dia** offers Lagos–Sagres cruises, barbecue cruises, dolphin safaris and grotto trips departing from the Lagos marina (tel: 282-764 670). **Mini Cruzeiros do Algarve** (Quay Q, Vilamoura Marina; tel: 289- 302 984) run a variety of coastal motor and sailing cruises.

Scuba-diving. Reef, night, wreck, cave and freshwater dives from near Lagos are offered by **Blue Ocean Divers** in Porto de Mós. They also cater for complete beginners (tel: 282-782 718). You can also explore the coastline with just a good snorkel and mask. Other centres include **Atlantic Diving** at Praia dos Aveiros and the **Divers' Cove** at Carvoeiro.

Spa. Not exactly a water sport per se, but the spa waters at Termas de Monchique (Caldas de Monchique) have drawn visitors since the 19th century. For more information on baths and fitness programmes, tel: 282-910 910.

Windsurfing. The most popular water sport along the Algarve coast – you'll find good instruction at Praia da Rocha,

Ferragudo, Praia da Luz, Praia de Faro and Quinta do Lago. The last two have both open sea and sheltered water, providing the luxury of calm conditions.

Outdoor Sports and Activities

Fishing. The waters of the Algarve provide some of the best big-game fishing in Europe. The Atlantic Ocean record, a blue marlin weighing more than 700kg (1,500lb), was caught just 8km (5 miles) off the coast of Faro in 1993. Shark (mostly blue, but occasionally copper, hammerhead, mako or tiger), marlin, billfish, large bass and giant conger are regularly hauled in. Swordfish and tuna can be caught further out.

Sagres, Portimão and Vilamoura are the main centres, where you can board a boat or hire a crew. One outfit to consider is the **Big Game Fishing Centre** in Praia da Rocha (Urb. Portas da Rocha, Lote 7; tel: 282-425 866).

Fishing on Fuzeta Beach

If the deep sea doesn't appeal, you can rent a small boat, rod and reel. The coast north of Sagres is one of the best spots to do this. You can also do as the locals do and use a rod and reel off the rocks at a harbour entrance or off the cliffs. Angling conditions are generally best in the winter, from October to mid-January.

Football. The Portuguese are wild about *futebol*, as

they call it, and the country hosted the European Football Championships in 2004. The biggest clubs are from the two major cities, Lisbon and Oporto. Both SC Farense and DC Louletano play at the Estadio do Algarve in Faro.

Horse Riding. Whether you're looking for pony rides for children, treks for the competent or hacks for the inexperienced, the mixed terrain of beaches, rolling hills and woods makes riding in the Algarve a delight. Most of the horses you'll encounter are at least part Lusitano, a sure-footed Portuguese breed. **Paraíso dos Cavalos** (Estrada de Almancil/Quinta do Lago; tel: 289-394 189) is highly regarded and offers a friendly and professional service. The **Quinta do Lago Riding Centre** (tel: 289-396 099), at Quinta do Lago near the Ria Formosa Nature Preserve, is also recommended, as are the schools at **Quinta Penedo** (in Vale Fuzeiros, near Albufeira; tel: 282-332 466) and **Centro Hípico Vale de Ferro** (Mexilhoeira Grande

---

Bullfighting

The main difference between the Portuguese and Spanish *corrida* is that in Portugal the bull leaves the ring bloodied but alive. Death does not come in the afternoon, but the following morning in the slaughterhouse. The Portuguese version is further sanitised in that the bull's horns are blunted to reduce the risk of injury by goring.

If you want the colour, spectacle and strategy of the bullfight but would prefer not to see the coup de grâce, then the Portuguese version may suit you. Be aware, though, that there is still a lot of blood, and the whole episode may well prove distasteful. The bull is used as a pincushion for long darts, then taunted and run to the ground. Bullfights are held most Saturdays, almost entirely for the benefit of curious tourists, at Lagos, Quarteira, Vila Real de Santo António and Albufeira. Look for notices advertising 'Praça de Touros'. The one in Albufeira, one of the best attended, is called Areias de São João (tel: 289-510 280).

between Lagos and Praia da Rocha). Also consider **Quinta da Gill**, Carvoeiro (on the N125) and **Tiffany's Riding Centre**, Vale Grifo, Almadena (between Sagres and Lagos; tel: 282-697 395).

Tennis. The most prestigious complex is the academy at **Vale do Lobo** (tel: 289-357 850), which has 14 all-weather courts, including six that are floodlit. Close by

Walkers admire the view at Fóia

is the well-equipped **Vilamoura Tennis Centre** (tel: 289-302 369), which has 12 courts. The **Jim Stewart Tennis Academy** at Quinta do Lago (tel: 289-398 848) has weekly coaching programmes on 10 hard and two synthetic grass courts. The **Carvoeiro Clube de Ténis** (tel: 282-357 847) on the outskirts of Carvoeiro has 14 courts as well as a pool and fitness centre.

Hotels with a good number of courts include the Alfa Mar, Praia da Falésia, near Olhos de Agua (18 courts); Hotel Alvor Praia, at Alvor beach (seven courts); and Hotel Montechoro, near Albufeira (eight courts). Instruction in the pleasant surroundings of the Ocean Club at Luz (five courts) is demanding but rewarding. Portimão has seven municipal hard courts available to guests (tel: 282-418 780 for booking).

Walking. The beaches and cliffs along the coast are excellent for walking, as are the mountains of the Serra do Monchique. A particularly good area for energetic walkers is near Praia da Luz, where you can climb 109m (358ft) from the beach or walk 3km (2 miles) to Porto de Mós or another 5km (3 miles) to Ponta da Piedade, near Lagos. A new long-distance footpath, the Via Algarviana, is being developed and will eventually link Cabo São Vicente with the Spanish border.

SHOPPING

Regional handicrafts range from copperware and cork to wickerwork and wine. The most famous items are *azulejos*.

What to Buy

Brass, Bronze and Copper. Candlesticks, pots and pans, old-fashioned kitchen scales, bowls and trays can be found. *Cataplanas* (bronze pressure-cookers used to make the national dish) make delightful decorative or functional souvenirs.

***Ceramics, Pottery and* Azulejos**. Portugal is renowned for its colourful, hand-painted and glazed pottery and tiles, and such items are generally much less expensive in Portugal than at home. The roadside potteries on the N125 in Porches are the best source of ceramics in the Algarve. You can buy a single blue-and-white tile *(azulejo)*, an address plaque for your house, or a batch to assemble into a picture when you get home. Or purchase an entire set of plates. With several days' notice some shops will paint tiles to order if you have a particular design in mind or they can copy a photograph. But remember that ceramics can be heavy and fragile to carry home; enquire about

Colourful hand-painted pottery from the Algarve

shipping; some potteries will take care of it for you.

Cork. Portugal is the world's leading producer of cork. You'll find place mats, intricate sculptures and other designs – and it's all as light as a feather.

Embroidery. Embroidered tablecloths, napkins and other items are found throughout the Algarve, especially at street markets, where they're likely to be literally thrust

Characterful pottery figures for sale in Moncarapacho

upon you. Haggling is absolutely acceptable at such places. Look also for the delicate hand needlework of the island of Madeira, items that are exceedingly well crafted but comparatively inexpensive.

Knitwear. Despite the generally warm weather along the Algarve, thick sweaters, caps and gloves, most of which come from the north of Portugal, are some of the region's few genuine bargains. Stalls at the suitably windy venues of Fóia and Sagres are surprisingly good value.

Leather. There was a time when leather goods were amazingly cheap in Portugal, but prices have risen considerably along with the tourist influx and 'Europeanisation'. Still, it's possible to find fashionable, relatively inexpensive shoes and handbags. Portimão is known for its selection of shops.

Rugs. Attractive and excellently crafted hand-made rugs, mostly from the Alentejo region (north of the Algarve), are made as beautifully as they have been for centuries. The name to look for is Arraiolos, a type of colourful, rustic-looking wool rug named after a small town.

Wicker. Bags, mats, furniture, plant-holders, glass- and wine-holders, trays – you name it, you're likely to find it.

Wine. Portugal's wine industry produces not only excellent table wines from regions such as the Dão, Douro and Alentejo, but legendary port wine, which comes from the north. Vintages of port all the way back beyond your birth year can still be found in dusty bottles, but they are expensive.

Where to Shop

Many shops on the Algarve stock pottery and leather items among the usual trinkets and souvenirs, but the most interesting spots for genuine handicrafts or local goods are regional markets. These colourful affairs are a mix of everyday wares for local consumption, genuine local handicrafts, leather goods and clothing. Usually held once or twice a month in the larger regional centres, they are popular with locals and tourists alike.

Another option is to go directly to the artisans' workshops. These are becoming increasingly difficult to find, as when the old craftsmen retire, their descendants are turning to tourism instead of the traditional ways. Loulé and Monchique are probably your best bets.

Pottery and ceramics are found in and around every resort, but route N125 along the coast sells more ceramics and pottery than almost anywhere else in Portugal. The small town of Porches has a couple of the top shops in the country: **Olaria Algarve** (Porches Pottery; tel: 282-352 858), which has revived and updated long-forgotten Moorish styles, and **Casa Algarve** (tel: 282-352 682). Another good source of hand-painted pottery is the very reasonably priced **Amó** (Sítio do Tonel, Sagres; tel: 282-624 748).

Good wine stores such as **Loja dos Vinhos** (Travessa dos Caldeireiros, Portimão; tel: 282-416 871) or **The Wine Shop** (Praça de Camões, Lagos) exist in all the big resorts.

ENTERTAINMENT

While Spain's southern coast is a magnet for ostentatious jet-setters who party all night, sophisticated nightlife has never really sprouted in the Algarve. Most evening entertainment is either hotel-based or set up specifically for tourists in bars and discos. But in quieter spots off the beaten tourist track and in less commercialised towns, you're more likely to find locals out for a drink.

Popular resorts such as Albufeira and Praia da Rocha throb nightly to a disco beat, while visitors in smaller and newer resorts may have to rely on their hotel for an evening's entertainment. Lagos is one of the few resorts with a good selection of low-key bars and live-music venues. The 'Strip' in the modern section of Albufeira and the tourist village of Montechoro abound with all-night drinking and dancing opportunities – few of them classy – for sun-scorched tourists.

Casinos operate at Praia da Rocha, Vilamoura and Monte Gordo. They have restaurants with floor shows (open to families), while gambling takes place in a separate gaming room, from mid-afternoon to well into the following morning. You must be 21 or over to gam-

An evening out in Lagos

ble and will need your passport or identity card. Dress is not formal but should be reasonably smart. Games include roulette, blackjack, baccarat and the Portuguese game of 'French bank'. The Casino in Praia da Rocha (Avenida Tomás Cabreira; tel: 282-415 999), open daily until 4am, is particularly popular.

Another favourite attraction is the *fado* night, at which distinctive Portuguese folk music is performed. You'll find them at bars and hotels. The quality of performances is unlikely to rival the clubs in Lisbon's atmospheric *bairros*, but you can still get a taste for this quintessentially Portuguese musical expression. There are two kinds of *fado*. First, the melancholic, nostalgia-tinged variety, whose origins are unclear, which may have developed as a form of mourning for men lost at sea or may be a relic of the days of slavery – a kind of Iberian blues. The other *fado* is much more upbeat, and, while lacking the

Folklore Shows

Folklore shows are regularly staged in the large resort hotels throughout the Algarve. Girls wear black felt hats over bright scarves, colourful blouses and aprons over skirts with hoops, and high-button shoes over white knitted stockings. The swift, whirling dances may also reveal traditional long underwear, worn in spite of the warm climate. Men are dressed more soberly, with trousers, waistcoats, cummerbunds and felt hats, mostly in black. Singers are accompanied by accordions, mouth organs and triangles.

There are basically two kinds of dances: the *corridinho*, or jig, which are whirling dances with stamping feet, and the *bailes de roda*, which are reels or square dances.

The Fonte Pequena restaurant in Alte hosts a lively folklore evening most nights. Look in local magazines for details of additional folklore events.

A traditional *fado* troupe

emotional power of the former, at least gives the audience a chance to wring out their handkerchiefs. Typically a *fado* troupe consists of a woman dressed in black accompanied by a couple of men playing acoustic guitars.

CHILDREN'S ALGARVE

The beaches of the Algarve, with long, sandy, gently shelving beaches for small children, and small rocky coves ideal for older children to explore, are perfect for family holidays. Pay attention to the beach warning flags, however. Green means the sea is calm and a lifeguard is on duty; green plus a checkered flag means that the lifeguard is not on duty; yellow urges caution; red means danger and warns bathers to stay ashore.

Water parks are the most popular choice for children away from the beach. There are several scattered across the Algarve; the best are **Slide & Splash** (N125 Vale de Deus, near Lagoa; tel: 282-341 685) and **Aqualand** (N125, near Alcantarilha;

tel: 282-322 827). Both offer a bus service all day from many points along the Algarve. **Atlantic Park** (Quatro Estradas, near Quarteira; tel: 289-397 757) has a mountain backdrop and features a daily high-diving show. Its neighbour, **Aquashow** (tel: 289-389 396), has fewer aquatic thrills, but both children and adults get the chance to drive scaled-down Formula 1 cars on a mini racing circuit (adults need driving licences).

Krazy World (along the Algoz-Messines road, north of Albufeira; tel: 282-574 134) has an animal farm, a miniature golf course, water scooters and swimming pools. **Montechoro Park** has an 18-hole mini-golf course, an Olympic-size swimming pool and many other facilities. Another attraction is **Zoomarine** (N125 at Guia, near Albufeira; tel: 289-560 301), a small amusement park with performing dolphins and sea lions, a parrot show, mini-zoo, cinema, various children's fairground rides and swimming pools.

For older children, sports such as tennis, horse riding, windsurfing and even golf may prove to be excellent diversions.

Several hotels in the Algarve are popular with families and well equipped for entertaining children. Most hotels in the Pestana chain, for example, have comprehensive 'Kids Club' programmes (with outdoor games, reading, treasure hunts, etc). Perhaps the best set up of all is the huge playground and day school at the upmarket **Sheraton Algarve** on Praia da Falésia. The hotel is one of the region's most luxurious, but in this case the children get as much out of it as the parents.

The Algarve's beaches are perfect for simple seaside fun

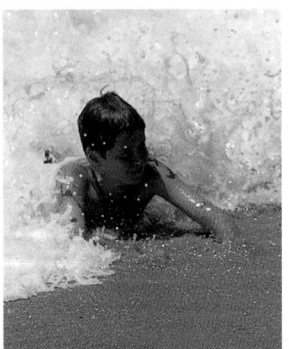

Calendar of Events

In comparison to the flamboyant fiestas of neighbouring Spain, Portugal's festivals are low-key. But each town celebrates at least once a year on its saint's day, so check at the tourist information office when you arrive for forthcoming events (a monthly events leaflet and other publications with listings are available).

February Lisbon: Fado Festival at various sites in the city.

February–March Loulé: *Carnaval* – parades and processions, spectacular flower-covered floats.

March Portugal Open – golf.

March–April Holy Week. Palm Sunday, Good Friday and Easter Day – services and processions.

April Loulé: Mãe Soberana – Pilgrimage to Nossa Senhora da Piedade.

May–June Various locations: Algarve International Music Festival – free classical concerts by local and international musicians, plus other performing arts, in some of the region's oldest churches; Alte: May Day festivities – folk dancing and markets; Estói: Festa da Pinha (Pine Festival) – wine and beer flow, along with barbecued chicken, dancers, accordianists and guitarists; Salir: Festa da Espiga – a procession followed by fireworks and folk dancing.

July Silves Castle: International Beer Festival; Loulé: International Jazz Festival; Faro: Senhora do Carmo – festivities and fair.

August Olhão: Shellfish Festival; Pinhal do Forte Novo, Quarteira: Sardine Festival; Castro Marim: Senhora dos Mártires – festivities and fair.

September Silves: Handicrafts Fair; Albufeira: Fishermen's festivals; throughout Algarve: National Folklore Festival – folk music and dance.

October Throughout Algarve: religious and trade fairs, including Feira de Outubro at Monchique (famous for its market) and the Feira de Santa Iria at Faro, a lively traditional event lasting several days; various locations: International Algarve Car Rally.

November Vilamoura: TAP Air Portugal Open Golf Championships.

December Igreja do Carmo, Tavira: Christmas choral concert.

EATING OUT

Most Algarve cooking is as unaffected as a fisherman's barbecue: grilled or fried fish, chicken and steaks. Which is not to say the Portuguese are not inventive; you'll sample combinations such as clams and pork, sole and bananas, or pork and figs.

You'll also find the spicy taste of Portugal's former colonies has crept into the national cuisine. Chicken *piri-piri* (made from Angolan peppers) is a hot and very popular dish in the Algarve. Curries occasionally appear on the menu, originating from the former colony of Goa (in southern India) or Africa.

But mostly, along the 160-km (100-mile) coast, you'll enjoy an excellent range of fresh fish and seafood. These items are no longer cheap, as much of it is now being brought in from distant waters. The humble but noble Portuguese sardine is an exception, and with a hunk of local rustic bread and a bottle of house wine, you can still feast well on a small budget.

Nearly every restaurant in Portugal serves a *couvert* (literally, cover) – an assortment of appetisers, including bread and butter, that appear to be free but are usually not. Your bill will include a charge of anywhere from €2 to €6 for the items. Theoretically, if you don't touch them, you shouldn't be charged for them.

Meal Times

Breakfast *(pequeno almoço)* is usually eaten any time up until about 10am. **Lunch** *(almoço)* is served from shortly after noon until 2.30pm, and **dinner** *(jantar)* runs from 7.30 to 10pm (or later in a *casa de fado*). Snacks between meals are usually taken at a *pastelaria* (pastry and cake shop), *salão de chá* (teashop), or what the Portuguese call a 'snack bar' – a stand-up counter selling sandwiches, savoury pastries and sweets.

Because lunch and dinner tend to be major events, you may prefer the kind of light breakfast the Portuguese eat: coffee, toast or rolls, butter and jam. Hotels usually provide large American-style buffets.

Starters

As soon as you sit down you will be served a pre-starter snack that may consist of bread, butter and a combination of olives, sardine paste and cream cheese (this isn't complimentary and will be on your bill as a cover charge).

Freshly caught sardines

Hearty starters always include a choice of soups – some vegetable soups, thickened with potatoes, can be almost a meal in themselves. Fish soup is variable but *gaspacho*, the Portuguese version of the cold Andalusian tomato-based soup, is usually good.

Fans of smoked food have two treats in store. The first is smoked ham *(presunto fumado)* – the best coming from Chaves, the northernmost province of Portugal (although Monchique ham is also highly regarded). The second is smoked swordfish *(espadarte fumado)*, which is a quite similar to smoked salmon but has a grainier texture and is less sweet. Most restaurants also have a range of international starters.

Cataplana – a regional dish

Fish and Seafood

Besides sardines, tuna is the top fish along the Algarve. It is usually served as a steak, with almonds, or in a thick stew (*estufado*). Prawns, crabs, lobsters and fresh fish are always their own best advertisement, and you will see them all over the Algarve either refrigerated in a window display or, in the case of large shellfish, counting their days in an aquarium waiting for your selection. Most shellfish and some fish are sold on a price-per-kilogram basis.

Lobster and fish priced on a weight basis are often brought to the table for a preview. Unless you happen to be on an expense account, this is the moment to ask the exact cost. Large shellfish can be very expensive, so make sure you get a proper answer to avoid problems when the bill arrives. There are two kinds of lobster: a *lavagante* (with large front claws) and the *lagostim* or *lagosta* (the spiny lobster or crayfish, without claws). Similarly, there are two kinds of crab: the *sapateira* is a big Atlantic type, the *santola* is a spider crab.

Look out for the following regional seafood dishes:

Açorda de marisco. A spicy, garlic-flavoured bread and seafood soup baked in a casserole, with raw eggs folded into the mixture at the table (also served as a starter).

Amêijoas à bulhão pato. Clams, fried or steamed with garlic and coriander.

Arroz de marisco. Seafood risotto.

Bife de Atum. A beefy fillet of tuna steak, marinated in wine or vinegar, salt, garlic and bay leaves, then cooked with onion and perhaps bacon.

Caldeirada de peixe. The Algarve version of the French bouillabaisse, a rich, filling mixed fish stew including potatoes, onions, tomatoes, peppers, wine and spices.

Cataplana. The region's most individual dish, named after the copper pressure-cooker in which it is prepared. The dish varies, but it is basically a combination of seafood, which always includes clams *(amêijoas)*, plus salami-style sausage, ham, onion, garlic, paprika, chilli, parsley and white wine.

Choquinhos con tinta. Cuttlefish served in their own ink.

Bacalhau

Cod, or *bacalhau*, is pretty much the national dish of Portugal. The Portuguese have been drying and salting cod since their first sea voyages to Newfoundland in 1501. Strangely, even though fresh fish is available on their own doorstep, they still prefer to ship in this relatively expensive, preserved fish. Preserving gives it a fuller flavour (though this is not always apparent when it is casseroled with many other ingredients). There are dozens of recipes for *bacalhau*, the most common on the Algarve being *à brás* – fried with onions and potatoes, then baked with a topping of beaten eggs.

Espadarte. Swordfish, often a grilled fillet steak. On some menus it's listed as *peixe agulha*. Don't confuse it with *peixe espada*, a long thin fish, usually translated as 'scabbard fish'.

Salada de polvo. Octopus salad.

Sardinhas. The best-value fish dish you'll enjoy on the Algarve; plump, juicy, crisply grilled and served with boiled potatoes. Note that fresh sardines are only available from June to October, though at Portimão you will get them year-round.

Meat and Poultry

Cabrito assado (no forno). Baked kid; not a common dish, but worth seeking out. *Cabrito estufado* is kid stewed with tomatoes and vegetables.

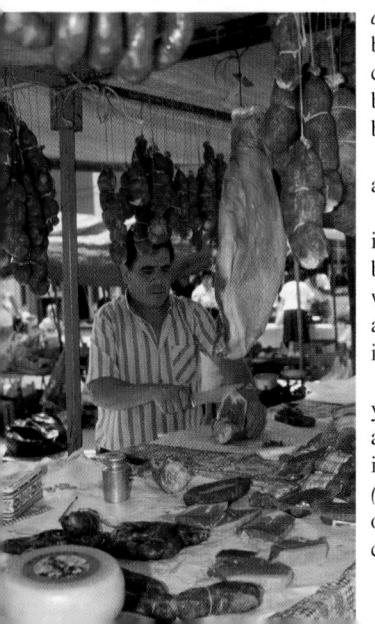

Fresh meat at the Loulé market

Carne de porco com amêijoas. An improbable but excellent combination of clams and roast pork, probably invented in the Alentejo, but adopted by the Algarve.

Favas à Algarvia. Pork and broad bean stew.

Feijoada. A hearty Brazilian dish consisting of dried beans and cabbage stewed with pork, sausage, bacon and whatever else of the pig is at hand (often the feet).

Frango piri-piri. What you most need to know about a *piri-piri* preparation is that it's hot. Chicken (*frango*), usually, is cooked or basted with tiny red chilli peppers from Angola (you'll see them strung as necklaces in the market).

Galinha cerejada. Roast chicken served with smoked meats and rice.

Leitão. Roast suckling pig, served hot or cold.

Bife/Steak à Portuguêsa. Steak fried with garlic, topped with ham and a fried egg, and served in a casserole dish surrounded by sautéed potatoes.

Fruits abound in the gentle Algarvian climate

Dessert

The Algarve, with a ready supply of almonds and figs, excels at sweet desserts. Both are employed in a variety of cakes and tarts, including *tarte de amêndoa,* almond tart. Other sweets worth trying are *arroz doce,* rice pudding topped with cinnamon; and *pudim flan,* crème caramel.

Portuguese cheese *(queijo)* is also an excellent dessert. The richest is *serra da estrela,* cured ewe's milk cheese from the country's highest mountains. It takes three hours to make each small cheese by hand and it is only available from December to April. Outside of this you'll have to make do with *tipo serra*, a harder, factory-made cheese. Other cheeses include *flamengo* (similar to Edam) and *saloio,* a creamy cottage cheese.

Table Wines

Portuguese wines, while not as well known as those from Spain and France, are uniformly good, and several regions produce truly excellent wines. You need only tell the waiter *tinto* (red) or *branco* (white) and you can't go wrong.

Vinho verde (green wine), produced in northwest Portugal, is a young white wine, slightly fizzy, light and delightful. A lesser-known type is red wine from the same region, bearing the seemingly oxymoronic name *vinho verde tinto* (red green wine). Both of these wines should be served chilled, as should Portuguese rosé, which is also slightly bubbly and may be either sweet or very dry. *Vinhos maduros* are mature, or aged, wines.

Vinho espumante is Portuguese sparkling wine, packaged in a Champagne-shaped bottle. Most are sweet but you can also find some relatively dry versions.

Several of the best wine-producing regions have names whose use is controlled by law *(região demarcada)*. The Dão and Douro in the north of Portugal produce vigorous reds and flavoursome whites. Wines from the Alentejo are also highly regarded. Of the local wines, you are most

Vineyard near Cacela Velha

likely to see the Lagoa label, packing more of a punch than average wine.

> Portuguese beers are good and refreshing. Light or dark, they are served chilled, bottled or from the tap. One of the best and most common is Sagres.

Other Alcoholic Drinks

The two most celebrated Portuguese wines, port and Madeira, are mostly known as dessert wines, but they may also be sipped as aperitifs. The before-dinner varieties are dry or extra dry white port, and the dry Madeiras, *Sercial* and *Verdelho*. These should be served slightly chilled. After dinner, sip one of the famous ruby or tawny ports (aged tawnys are especially good) or a Madeira dessert wine, such as *Boal* or *Malvasia* (Malmsey). Two local wines that make excellent aperitifs are *Algar Seco* and *Afonso III*. Reminiscent of sherry, both come from Lagoa and are served chilled.

Local after-dinner specialities include *aguardente de medronho,* a brandy distilled from the fruit of the arbutus tree. Blended with honey, it's called *medronheira de mel.* Equally powerful is *bagaço,* or *bagaceira,* a firewater made from grape residue in the same way as the French make *marc* and the Italians *grappa*.

Coffee and Tea

When they want a coffee, most Portuguese order a *bica,* which is a small espresso. If that's a little too small for you, order a *duplo,* a double. Take one *bica*, add water, and you have a *carioca*; a few drops of milk transforms it into a *garoto*.

A white coffee in a café is a *galão*, served in a tall glass. In a restaurant you would order a *café com leite*. Tea *(chá)* has been drunk in Portugal as long as it has been known to the Western world.

To Help You Order ...

Could we have a table?	**Queremos uma mesa.**
Do you have a set-price menu?	**Tem uma ementa turística?**
I'd like a/an/some ...	**Queria ...**

beer	**uma cerveja**	mineral water	**água mineral**
the bill	**a conta**	napkin	**guardanapo**
bread	**pão**	salad	**salada**
butter	**manteiga**	salt	**sal**
dessert	**sobremesa**	sandwich	**sanduíche**
fish	**peixe**	soup	**sopa**
fruit	**fruta**	sugar	**açúcar**
ice cream	**gelado**	tea	**chá**
meat	**carne**	vegetables	**legumes**
menu	**a carta**	wine	**vinho**
milk	**leite**	wine list	**carta de vinhos**

... and Read the Menu

alho	garlic	**lombo**	fillet
ameijoas	baby clams	**lulas**	squid
arroz	rice	**mariscos**	shellfish
assado	roast	**mexilhões**	mussels
bacalhau	codfish	**ovo**	egg
besugo	sea bream	**ostras**	oysters
dobrada	tripe	**pescada**	hake
dourada	sea bass	**pescadinha**	whiting
feijões	beans	**polvos**	baby octopus
frito	fried	**queijo**	cheese
gambas	prawns	**salmonete**	red mullet
lagosta	spiny lobster	**truta**	trout
lenguado	sole	**vitela**	veal

HANDY TRAVEL TIPS

An A–Z Summary of Practical Information

A

ACCOMMODATION (see also CAMPING, YOUTH HOSTELS and RECOMMENDED HOTELS)

Besides hotels, which range in an official category from 1 to 5 stars (not directly related to price), you'll find *aparthotels* (one- or two-bedroom with kitchenette, occasionally called *aldeamentos*) as well as a selection of accommodation variously categorised by overlapping and confusing names. A small, basic guest house is labelled a *pensão* or *residencial* (pension); *quinta* and *estalagem* refer to an inn or rural estate, and *albergaria* is generally a 4–5 star inn. A *pousada* is a government-owned (but now privately managed) hotel, often but not always in an historic building. There are just two in the Algarve, in Sagres and Sao Brás de Alportel, but look for a couple more to be opened – in the Palace of Estói and a former convent near the castle in Tavira – in the near future.

Many tour operators book blocks at large, modern (and often undistinguished) hotels on or near beaches. If you wish to be on the beach, make sure that what is described as a 'sea view' is not one that requires binoculars to see the distant ocean.

I'd like a single/double room.	**Queria um quarto simples/duplo.**
with bath/shower	**com banho/chuveiro**
What's the rate per night?	**Qual é o preço por noite?**

AIRPORT (*aeroporto*)

Faro International Airport, serving the Algarve, is 7km (4 miles) from Faro, the regional capital. It's just a 10-minute taxi ride to Faro, and about half an hour by car to Albufeira. There's also a bus service to Faro. Several international and local car-hire agencies have service desks at the airport. The airport tourist information office will assist you with finding accommodation and any other queries. Elsewhere in the terminal are a post office, bank, ATM, a choice of restaurants and snack bars, newsstand, shops and duty-free.

Airport Information, tel: 289-800 800 (arrival and departure times, tel: 289-800 801).

TAP Air Portugal reservations, tel: 289-800 731; <www.tap.pt>.

PGA Portugalia reservations, tel: 289-800 851; <www.pga.pt>.

Where can I get a taxi?	**Onde posso encontrar um taxi?**
Please take these bags.	**Leve-me a baggagem, por favor.**

B

BICYCLE HIRE *(aluguer de bicicleta)*

Most resort hotels have bicycles for hire. If yours does not, the major resorts all have scooter and bike rental shops. Among those are Quiosqe Navegador, in Sagres (Rua Comandante Matoso; tel: 282-624 751), Mourabike in Vilamoura (tel: 91-727 0801) and Motoride in Lagos (Rua José Afonso, 23; tel: 282-761 720). Expect to pay €8.50–10 per day.

BUDGETING FOR YOUR TRIP

The season when you go will have much to do with the cost of your trip. Hotel rates rise astonishingly during the summer months.

Getting to the Algarve. Many Europeans fly direct to Faro aboard regularly scheduled and charter flights. Scheduled flights from the UK and continental Europe cost around €60–600 return. The national airline, TAP Air Portugal (<www.tap.pt>) operates daily flights from Heathrow direct to Faro, British Airways (<www.ba.com>) has a daily service from Gatwick. For low-cost fares try EasyJet (<www.easyjet.com>) and Monarch Airlines (<www.flymonarch.com>). For those travelling from beyond Europe, the flight will be a higher proportion of your overall budget – though scheduled flights from North America can often be bought for €500–700 return, outside the high season. Economical package deals – airline and hotel – are usually available.

Accommodation. Hotels at the top levels are comparable to large European cities. In high summer season (July–August especially), hotel prices are exorbitant – often double what they cost in off-season. Outside high season, many hotels at the two-, three- and four-star ratings are excellent value. In high season, a double room with bath per night in a 3-star hotel averages €100–40; 4-star hotel, €150–200; 5-star hotel, €250–500. *Pousadas* generally range from €140–90 for a double room.

Meals. Even top-rated restaurants may be surprisingly affordable compared to most European cities. Portuguese wines are quite good and very attractively priced, even in fine restaurants. A three-course meal with wine in a reasonable establishment averages about €20–30 per person. Most hotels offer half- and full-board plans. Continental or full-buffet breakfast is nearly always included in the price of hotels.

Local transport. Buses and taxis are reasonably priced. Local buses are less than €2; a taxi costs €3–10 for most fares within a resort or town (a supplement of 20 percent is levied on weekends, public holidays and between 10pm and 6am). Taxis can be hired for day trips for set fees; check with the local tourist office for a list of trips.

Car hire. It's a good idea to hire a car in order to allow maximum flexibility, but be sure to budget for the cost of petrol, which is costly, as in most of Europe. Economy car hire is cheaper than in most parts of Europe; expect it to run between €20 and €50 per day (including collision insurance and taxes). You may find even better bargains at local firms.

Organized excursions. These cost €15–20 for a half day, €35–45 for a whole day, including lunch.

Activities. It costs about €50–150 for *golf* for an 18-hole championship course (or €45–75 for 9 holes); €65–80 per day for *big-game fishing* (spectators €40); *horse riding*, €15–25 per hour; and *tennis* €8–14 per hour per court. Instruction for most sports ranges from €25–40 per hour.

Nightlife and entertainment. Costs vary widely. Expect cover fees at discos to range from €8–15, which usually includes first drink; casino entrance is roughly €15. Entrance to waterparks generally costs around €17 for adults and €10 for children.

C

CAMPING *(campismo)*

Many of the Algarve's two dozen camp sites are within easy reach of a beach. They range from very cheap, basic grounds to vast recreational centres with restaurants, pools and sports facilities. Sites belonging to clubs or the Portuguese Camping Federation are open to holders of a Camping Carnet. There are also a number of private sites that may only be used by members of the respective owners' associations.

Camping on beaches, or indeed anywhere outside recognised sites, is illegal. Details on all Algarve campsites are available from tourist information offices or contact Roteiro Campista, Apartado 3168, 1301–902 Lisbon, <www.roteiro-campista.pt>, for information and prices.

Is there a campsite near here?	**Há algum parque de campismo por aqui perto?**
May we camp here?	**Podemos acampar aqui?**
We have a caravan (trailer).	**Temos uma caravana.**

CAR HIRE *(de aluguer;* see also DRIVING)

Cars can be picked up at the main airports where the major car-hire companies have their outlets. However it is normally cheaper to reserve a car in advance. Holiday Autos (<www.holidayautos.com>, tel: 0870 400 4468 in the UK) offer some of the cheapest rates.

You must be at least 21 and have held a valid national (or international) driving licence for at least one year. Rental companies will accept your home country national driver's licence. Third-party insurance is included in the basic charge but a collision damage waiver (CDW) and personal accident policy may be added. You will need to present a recognised credit card or a significant cash deposit when booking.

A value-added tax (IVA) is added to the total charge, but will have been included if you have pre-paid the car hire before arrival. Third-party insurance is required and included, but full collision coverage is advisable as well. Many credit cards automatically include this if you use the card to pay for the car, but be sure to verify this before you leave home.

You can drive in Spain at no extra charge but be sure to inform the company you are going there when booking the car. A basic economy car is likely to average €20–50 per day (including collision insurance and taxes). There is a small additional charge for an extra driver. Make sure you return the car with a full tank of fuel – there are hefty charges if you fail to do so.

I'd like to hire a car	**Queria alugar um carro**
for today/tomorrow	**para hoje/amanhã**
for one day/a week	**por um dia/uma semana**
Please include full insurance.	**Que inclua um seguro contra todos os riscos, por favor.**

CLIMATE

The Algarve's climate is generally warm all year round, with rare extremes. Winter evenings can occasionally be rather chilly, and hot periods in July and August may prove stifling to those who prefer milder weather. Spring and autumn are the best seasons to travel in the Algarve.

Air temperature											
J	F	M	A	M	J	J	A	S	O	N	D
°C 12	12	14	15	18	21	23	24	22	18	15	13
°F 54	54	57	59	64	69	73	75	72	64	59	55

Sea temperature											
°C 15	16	17	18	19	21	21	20	19	18	16	14
°F 59	61	62	64	66	69	69	67	66	64	61	57

CLOTHING *(roupa)*

Dress is casual in almost all parts of the Algarve. The exceptions are certain luxury hotels and restaurants, as well as casinos, where smart (though never formal) attire is appreciated.

Pack a sweater or jacket, even in summer, as evenings can turn quite cool. Winters are mild with the occasional shower, so a light rainproof jacket may come in handy. It's cooler in the mountains and also in Lisbon and its environs, so dress warmer if you plan on including these.

CRIME AND SAFETY *(segurança*; see also EMERGENCIES and POLICE)

As a major tourist area, the Algarve experiences more petty crime than other parts of Portugal, though crimes involving violence against tourists are very rare. Theft from hire cars is the most common crime targeting tourists. In rural areas the problem is far less acute, but in resorts and where cars are left unattended for a period of time (at beach parking areas, beauty spots, etc) the risk is high.

Burglaries of holiday apartments, though less common than car theft, also occur, so be on your guard to the best extent possible.

As a rule, never leave anything in your car, even if it is out of sight and locked in the boot. Keep valuables in the hotel safe and refrain from carrying large sums of money or wearing expensive jewellery on the street. Do not leave bags and cameras unattended on the beach.

Report any theft to the hotel receptionist, the nearest police station, or the local tourist office. You must report any losses to the local police within 24 hours and obtain a copy of your statement for insurance purposes.

If you are going to Lisbon, beware that the city is infamous for its pickpockets, particularly on the Metro, the buses and Rossio square. You are also advised not to walk in the Bairro Alto or Alfama areas at night unless in a group.

I want to report a theft.	**Quero participar um roubo.**

CUSTOMS AND ENTRY REQUIREMENTS (*alfândega*)

Americans, British, Canadians and many other nationalities need only a valid passport – no visa – to visit Portugal. EU nationals may enter with an identity card. The length of stay authorised for most tourists is 90 days (60 for US and Canadian citizens).

The Portuguese–Spanish border scarcely serves as a frontier anymore and visitors can come and go easily, though you should carry identification.

Currency restrictions. Visitors from within the EU can bring in or exit Portugal with any amount of local or foreign currency, but sums exceeding the equivalent of €5,000 in foreign currency from outside the EU should be declared on arrival.

Customs. Free exchange of non-duty-free goods for personal use is permitted between Portugal and other EU countries. However, duty-free items are subject to restrictions: check before you go.

I've nothing to declare.	**Não tenho nada a declarar.**
It's for my personal use.	**É para uso pessoal.**

D

DRIVING (see also CAR HIRE and EMERGENCIES)

Driving can be the best way to see the Algarve, but, especially in high season, traffic can test one's patience. It can also be costly, as petrol and rental charges are likely to outpace the cost of public transport.

Road conditions. The southern Algarve coastline is served by the Nacional 125 (abbreviated to the 'N125'). Parallel to this road is the new E01 (also called the Via do Infante, IP1), which runs from Spain as far west as Lagos. This road links in with the A2 motorway going north to Lisbon. The Via do Infante has helped divert traffic from the N125, which in summer can become a bumper-to-bumper nightmare. Exercise care at all times on this road; the accident rate is one of the highest in Europe.

In rural areas, beware of such rustic hazards as herds of sheep or goats around the next bend, unlit donkeys and carts at night, tractors, hay carts, etc. If driving to Lisbon, allow at least three hours. In high season the motorway can be quite congested, and once you reach the centre of Lisbon traffic slows to a crawl.

Rules and regulations. The rules of the road are the same as in most Western European countries. At roundabouts the vehicle on the roundabout has priority unless road markings or lights indicate otherwise. Local driving standards are improving but are still erratic. Speed limits are 120kph (75mph) on motorways, 90kph (56mph) on other roads and 50kph (37mph) in urban areas. Cars towing caravans (trailers) are restricted to 50kph (31mph) in towns and 70kph (45mph) on the open road and motorways. Most motorways have tolls *(portagems)*. The Portuguese routinely disregard speed limits, but that doesn't mean you should.

Seat belts are mandatory, and children under 12 cannot sit in the front seat unless strapped into a special child restraint. You can be fined on the spot for not carrying your licence, passport, or car-rental documents; for ignoring parking restrictions; and for drink-driving (limit 0.5mg/l).

If you take your own car, you need only your national driving licence, car registration papers and the Green Card extension to your insurance – third party is obligatory, and comprehensive coverage is highly recommended. A warning triangle is also compulsory.

Fuel. Fuel by the litre is expensive in Portugal. Prices should be the same – or very close to it – everywhere you go. Some petrol stations are 24-hour, and all accept credit cards. Filling up anywhere near the N125 is easy, but petrol stations are sparse in some inland regions.

Parking. Parking in most towns and resorts is manageable. Don't disregard no-parking signs: your car may be towed away. Certain areas are metered and others are 'Blue Zones' where you must buy a ticket from a machine. Car parks and garages are also available.

If you need help. There are SOS telephones stationed about every 3km (2 miles) on main roads. If you belong to a motoring organisation affiliated with the Automóvel Clube de Portugal (in Lisbon, Rua Rosa Araújo 24; tel: 213-180 100), you can make use of their services free of charge. The emergency number for police and ambulance is **112**.

Road signs. Standard international pictograms are used in Portugal, but you might also encounter the following signs:

alto	halt
cruzamento	crossroads
curva perigosa	dangerous bend
desvio	diversion
encruzilhada	crossroads
estacionamento permitido	parking allowed
estacionamento proíbido	no parking
guiar com cuidado	drive with care
obras/fim de obras	road works (men working)/ end of road works

paragem de autocarro	sus stop
pare	stop
passagem proíbida	no entry
pedestres/peões	pedestrians
perigo	danger
posto de socorros	first-aid post
proibida a entrada	no entry
saída de camiões	lorry (truck) exit
seguir pela direita/esquerda	keep right/left
sem saída	no through road
sentido proíbido	no entry
sentido único	one-way street
silêncio	silence zone
stop	stop
trabalhos	road works (men working)
trânsito proíbido	no through traffic
velocidade máxima	maximum speed

Are we on the right road for …?	**É esta a estrada para …?**
Fill the tank with super, please.	**Encha o depósito de super, por favor.**
Check the oil/tyres/ battery, please.	**Verifique o óleo/os pneus/ a bateria, se faz favor.**
I've broken down.	**O meu carro está avariado.**
There's been an accident.	**Houve um acidente.**

E

ELECTRICITY *(electricidade, luz)*

Standard throughout Portugal is 220-volt, 50-cycle AC. US and British appliances may require an adaptor, and those from North America will also need a transformer.

EMBASSIES AND CONSULATES *(embaixada; consulado)*

Consulates in the Algarve:

British Consulate (Consulado da Grã Bretanha, which handles Commonwealth nationals): Largo Francisco A Maurício, 7, 1°; Portimão; tel: 282-490 750.

Canadian Consulate (Consulado de Canadá): Rua Aboim Ascensão, 87; Faro; tel: 289-803 757).

Embassies in Lisbon:

Australia: Av. da Liberdade 200; tel: 213-101 500.

Canada (Embassy/Consulate): Av. da Liberdade 144, 3°; tel: 213-164 600.

Republic of Ireland (Embassy/Consulate): Rua da Imprensa à Estrela 1; tel: 213-929 440.

South Africa (Embassy): Avenida Luís Bivar 10/10 A; tel: 213-192 200.

United Kingdom (Embassy): Rua de São Bernardo 33; tel: 213-924 000.

USA (Embassy/Consulate): Avenida das Forças Armadas 16; tel: 217-273 300.

Most embassies and consulates are open Mon–Fri from 9 or 10am until 4.30 or 5pm, with a break in the middle of the day of 1–3 hours.

EMERGENCIES *(urgência)*

Dial **112** for medical, police and general emergencies in all Portugal.

The hospitals at Faro and Portimão have *bancos de urgência* (emergency wards). Some hospitals can also handle dental emergencies. For trouble on the road such as a breakdown, see DRIVING.

G

GAY AND LESBIAN TRAVELLERS

In a country heavily influenced by the Catholic Church, attitudes towards gays are not as tolerant as elsewhere in Europe, though in tourist-dominated enclaves of the Algarve, such as 'the Strip' in

Albufeira, gay travellers will find accommodating bars and restaurants. The website <www.portugalgay.pt> contains a travel guide with information in English and other languages. It has some specific information relating to the Algarve and a message board.

GETTING TO THE ALGARVE (see also AIRPORT)

Air Travel. Regular scheduled, cheap charter flights fly to Faro (mostly in summer) from the UK, Ireland and most major cities in Western Europe. Scheduled flights by TAP Air Portugal and British Airways are more expensive, though they usually offer special deals outside high season.

TAP Air Portugal (tel: 707-205 700 anywhere in Portugal; 800-221 7370 anywhere in the US; 0845-601 0932 in the UK) is the national Portuguese airline. From the US to Lisbon, it flies direct daily from New York, Newark. Continental also flies direct to Lisbon from New York, Newark. These and many other airlines make connections in Lisbon and travel on to Faro. Travellers originating their journeys in Canada, Australia, New Zealand or South Africa will connect to Lisbon or Faro in London or another major European city.

Faro International Airport is 7km (4 miles) from Faro, the regional capital. For airport information, tel: 289-800 800.

By car. Many travellers each year take their cars from other points in Europe by major highways through Spain and Portugal. British travellers can take their car across the Channel to France or Belgium and make the drive from there, although the trip is likely to take 3 or 4 days.

The distance from Calais to the Algarve is over 2,000km (1,300 miles), so you might like to consider the long-distance car-ferry service from Plymouth to Santander in northern Spain (a 19-hour trip). From Santander follow the N611 and then the E3 via Valladolid and Coimbra. See the information below on ferries, under 'By Sea'.

By rail. The Portuguese national railway network is called **Caminhos de Ferro Portugueses** (tel: 808-208 208; <www.cp.pt>). Portugal is linked to the European railway network; connections to Lisbon are possible from points throughout Spain, France and the rest of continental Europe. Travel to and within Portugal is included on any InterRail or EurailPass; the Eurodomino pass is available for travel within Portugal only for a 3–8-day period, but may not be as good a deal as it is on more expensive rail networks in northern Europe.

London to Paris by rail takes around 20 hours, going via Eurostar to Paris, from Paris to Irún on the Spanish border by TGV and from Irún to Lisbon on the Sud-Express. Lisbon and the Algarve are now linked by a direct, high-speed train. The service departs from Lisbon's new Oriente station. The journey time to Faro has been reduced to 3½ hours.

By Sea. Lisbon is a major port, and several cruise ships include a port-of-call in the capital. From Britain, Brittany Ferries (<www.brittany-ferries.co.uk>) sails twice weekly from Plymouth (around 19 hours) and P&O Ferries (<www.poferries.com>) goes from Portsmouth to Bilbao (28 hours) in Spain. Both services operate twice weekly from March to December. The drive from Bilbao to the Algarve is likely to take another 15 to 18 hours.

GUIDES AND TOURS *(guias; visitas guiadas)*

A number of guided day-trip itineraries are available through almost all hotels and a myriad of local travel agencies and tour operators. These include: Seville in Spain, Lisbon, the River Guadiana, Silves and Monchique, Sagres, Lagos and the west, Loulé market and Alte, and jeep safaris. If you would like a personal guide to a particular place, the nearest tourist office or travel agency should be able to direct you to qualified local guides. Day trips can be arranged with taxi drivers at set fees; again, see the local tourist information office for details.

Boat trips exploring the nooks and crannies of the famous Barlavento (west) coast are a popular choice; they depart from several points west of Vilamoura, most notably from Portimão.

Tourism offices in Albufeira, Tavira, Faro and São Brás de Alportel offer guided walks of the historical centres of towns.

We'd like an English-speaking guide/an English interpreter.	**Queremos uma guia que fale inglês /um intérprete de inglês.**

H

HEALTH AND MEDICAL CARE (see also EMERGENCIES)

Standards of hygiene are generally very high; the most likely illness to befall travellers will be due to an excess of sun or alcohol. Tap water is safe to drink, but bottled water is always safest and is available everywhere. Even most local people drink bottled water, either *água com gas* (carbonated) or *sem gas* (still). Mosquitoes are common in summer; an anti-mosquito device that plugs into your wall and emits a vapour noxious to the insect but not to you, is available at airport shops.

Farmácias (chemists) are open during normal business hours and are recognisable by an illuminated green cross sign. At other times one shop in each neighbourhood is on duty round the clock. Addresses are listed in newspapers. To locate night pharmacies, tel: 118.

For more serious illness or injury, all principal Algarve towns and resorts have hospitals, and many doctors are multilingual (most can speak English remarkably well). There are also a number of expatriate doctors at medical clinics and health centres throughout the region. Tourist offices carry lists of English-speaking doctors. The Red Cross *(Cruz Vermelha)* can be contacted in Faro (tel: 289-899 900) and Portimão (tel: 282-485 640).

Medical insurance to cover illness or accident while abroad is a good investment. EU nationals with a European Health Insurance Card (EHIC) obtained well before departure can receive free emergency treatment at Social Security and Municipal hospitals in Portugal. Privately billed hospital visits are expensive.

Where's the nearest (all-night) pharmacy?	**Onde fica a farmácia (de serviço) mais próxima?**
I need a doctor/dentist.	**Preciso de um médico/uma dentista.**
I'm not feeling well.	**Não me sinto bem.**
an ambulance	**ambulância**
hospital	**hospital**

HOLIDAYS *(feriado)*

National holidays:

1 January	*Ano Novo*	New Year's Day
25 April	*Dia da Liberdade*	Revolution Day
1 May	*Dia do Trabalho*	Labour Day
10 June	*Dia de Portugal*	National Day
15 August	*Assunção*	Assumption
5 October	*Heróis da República*	Republic Day
1 November	*Todos-os-Santos*	All Saints' Day
1 December	*Dia da Independência*	Independence Day
8 December	*Imaculada Conceição*	Immaculate Conception
25 December	*Natal*	Christmas Day

Movable dates:

Carnaval	Shrove Tuesday
Sexta-feira Santa	Good Friday
Corpo de Deus	Corpus Christi

In addition, every town closes down and takes to the streets at least once a year in honour of its own patron saint. See the Calendar of Events for other events *(page 93)*.

Are you open tomorrow?	**Estão abertos amanhã?**
When do you close?	**Quando fecha?**

L

LANGUAGE

Your senior-school Spanish may help with signs and menus, but will not unlock the mysteries of spoken Portuguese. The Portuguese in Portugal is much more closed and gutteral-sounding and is also spoken much faster than that in Brazil. A surprising number of people in the Algarve speak passable and even fluent English. The *Berlitz Portuguese Phrasebook & Dictionary* covers most situations you're likely to encounter during a visit to Portugal.

M

MAPS

The Algarve is a relatively small region, linked east to west by the N125, so orientation is easy. The red, green and yellow 'Portugal Tourist Map', available at some tourist information offices, is a map of the entire country; you may need a magnifying glass for the smaller roads in the Algarve. Otherwise, to explore roads less travelled, the 'Turinta' map of the Algarve (1:176,000) is a good buy. All tourist information offices will supply you with a reasonable street plan of the local town.

a street map of…	**uma planta de…**
a road map of the Algarve	**um mapa das estradas do Algarve**

MEDIA *(jornal; revista)*

Foreign newspapers usually arrive the day after publication, though European editions of the *Guardian* and *Financial Times* and the *International Herald Tribune* are available on the same day at many newsagents. Popular foreign magazines are also available. The most important Portuguese-language daily is *Diário de Notícias,* which contains full cultural listings. Popular foreign magazines and paperback books in English are also available.

English-language publications with useful information as to what's on (folklore, markets, music, cinema, sporting events, etc) include: *The Algarve News*, a bi-weekly newspaper; the *Algarve Resident*, a weekly magazine; and *Welcome to the Algarve*, a monthly free newspaper/information sheet. *Algarve Tips*, a 150-page booklet distributed free of charge at many hotels, also has a wealth of useful listings.

There are two government-operated TV channels in Portugal. Most large hotels and some bars also have satellite TV showing feature films, football games and other big sporting events. For the BBC World Service, with news on the hour, tune in to 648 kHz medium wave. The *Anglo-Portuguese News* gives details of programmes and wavelengths.

MONEY (*dinheiro*; see also BUDGETING FOR YOUR TRIP)

Currency (*moeda*). The euro (€) is the official currency used in Portugal. Notes are denominated in 5, 10, 20, 50, 100 and 500 euros; coins in 1 and 2 euros and 1, 2, 5, 10, 20 and 50 cents (*cêntimos*).

Currency exchange (*banco; câmbio*). Normal banking hours are Monday–Friday 8.30am–3pm. Some banks remain open later and at weekends to change money. The exchange at Faro airport is open daily 6am–midnight. Changing money can be quite expensive, and you are advised to check the rate of commission before any transaction. Banks often levy 0.5 percent commission with a minimum charge of €10, so it is not a good idea to exchange small amounts with them. Automatic money-exchanging machines (ATMs) charge at least 2 percent commission.

At the time of going to press, US $1 = €0.80; £1 = €1.40.

Credit cards (*cartão de crédito*). Standard international credit cards are widely accepted, as are Eurocheque cards. However, in some shops and restaurants, especially in small villages, you may not be able to use a credit card.

ATMs *(caixa automática)*. Automatic teller machines outside banks, identified by the MB (MultiBanco) sign, are widely available. You can get cash with a Visa or Mastercard or other card on one of the international networks like Cirrus, as long as your card has a four-digit PIN.

Travellers' cheques. Travellers' cheques can be cashed at any bank, though a high flat-rate fee is charged for changing them. Paying by cheque is invariably more expensive than by cash, due to the lower rate of exchange. You will need to show your passport.

Can I pay with this credit card?	**Posso pagar com cartão de crédito?**
I want to change some pounds/dollars.	**Queria trocar libras/dólares.**
Can you cash a traveller's cheque?	**Pode pagar um cheque de viagem?**

O

OPENING HOURS *(horas de abertura)*

Most shops and offices open 9am–1pm and 3–7pm weekdays and 9am–1pm Saturday. In summer many shops will remain open all day, and until 10pm or later. Most museums close for lunch, from noon or 12.30pm to 2 or 2.30pm, but major ones stay open all day. Most public museums are closed on Monday. Churches normally open from 7am–noon and 4–7pm Monday to Saturday and are open for Mass on Sunday.

The Portuguese do not take a siesta, but most businesses close for a 1–2-hour lunch break. Banks are open 8.30am–3pm Monday–Friday. In resorts many bars are open from noon (or earlier) until the wee hours. Informal restaurants may open all day but more upscale establishments may only open at lunch and in the evening, or for dinner only. Some restaurants close one day a week, so check first.

P

POLICE (*polícia*; see also EMERGENCIES)

Police wearing armbands marked CD (it stands for Corpo Distrital, meaning local corps) are assigned to assist tourists and normally speak at least a smidgen of a foreign language. On highways, traffic is controlled by the Guarda Nacional Republicana (GNR) in white cars or on motorcycles. For a general emergency, dial 112.

Where's the nearest police station?	**Onde fica o posto de policia mais próximo?**

POST OFFICES (*correios*)

Post offices are indicated by the letters CTT (*Correios, Telegrafos e Telefones*). The mail service is generally good, though it can get bogged down during the height of the season. Most postboxes follow the British pillar-box design and are painted bright red.

Main offices open 8.30 or 9am to 6 or 6.30pm Monday–Friday; local branches open 9am to 12.30pm and 2 to 6pm Monday–Friday. The main post offices in Portimão and Faro open on Saturday mornings as well. You can also buy stamps from most shops.

Mail from Portugal may take up to a week to reach a European destination. There is also a following-day 'Azul' (express) service.

Where's the nearest post office?	**Onde fica a estação de correios mais próxima?**
A stamp for this letter/ postcard, please.	**Um selo para esta carta/este postal, por favor.**
express (special delivery)	**expresso**
airmail	**via aérea**
registered	**registado**

PUBLIC TRANSPORT

Buses (*autocarro*). EVA Transportes (<www.eva-bus.net>) operates most buses in the Algarve. Local and regional timetables may be consulted at any bus station or tourist information office. Most buses run on time. Buy your ticket on board the bus for all services except for the Algarve Express, where tickets must be purchased in advance at the station. Bus stops are denoted by the sign 'Paragem'.

Trains (*comboio*). An Algarve railway line runs from Lagos in the west to the eastern frontier at Vila Real de Santo António, with 50 stations in between. Stations are in or near Faro, Portimão and Lagos, but in other spots are far enough away to require a bus or taxi ride. The most notable example is the station of Albufeira, which is actually near Ferreiras and a good 15-minute bus ride from the resort. The link between the Algarve and Lisbon has been dramatically improved. Trains now depart from the new Oriente station in Lisbon and the journey to the Algarve junction Tunes has been cut to 3 hours. For Faro add another 30 minutes. A return Lisbon–Faro fare is €47.

Train timetables are posted at all railway stations; request a *guía de horarios* for a full listing of timetables. Consult the website of Caminhos de Ferro Portugueses, the national railway network, for timetables and information on international and domestic trains: <www.cp.pt>.

Taxis (*táxi*). Portuguese taxis are usually cream-coloured though some of the old black and green ones are still in use. While you can hail them in the street, it is usually easier to go to a taxi stand or telephone for one. The majority of taxis are metered. If your taxi does not have a meter, make sure you ask what the charge will be before setting out. Average taxi fares to all resorts from Faro are posted at the airport. Luggage is free of charge but fares increase by 20 percent if you travel from 10pm to 6am.

Where can I get a taxi?	**Onde posso encontrar um táxi?**
What's the fare to…?	**Quanto custa o percurso para…?**
Where is the nearest railway station/bus stop?	**Onde é a estação ferroviária/ a paragem de autocarros mais próxima?**
When's the next bus/train to…?	**Quando parte o próximo autocarro/comboio para…?**
I want a ticket to…	**Queria um bilhete para…**
single (one-way trip)	**ida**
return (round-trip)	**ida e volta**

R

RELIGION

The Portuguese are predominantly Roman Catholic, a fact reflected in surviving religious rituals and saints' days that are public holidays. Services in English are scheduled in principal tourist areas. Protestant (primarily Anglican) services are held in several towns. Full details of all services are available from tourist offices and most hotels; the free monthly *Welcome to the Algarve* also carries an abbreviated listing, and *Algarve Resident* has a full one.

T

TELEPHONE *(telefone)*

Portugal's country code is 351. There are no local dialling codes; you need to dial all 9 digits from anywhere within the country.

Most public telephones accept pre-paid telephone cards or credit cards. *Credifone* telephone cards can be purchased at post offices, newsagents or cafés. Local, national and international calls can also be made from hotels, but almost always with an exorbitant surcharge.

You are wise to make these with an international calling card, if you must make them from your hotel room.

To call from a public phonebox, pick up the receiver, insert card or coin, wait for the dial tone and dial. To make an international call, dial 00 for an international line (both Europe and overseas; eg. UK 0044, USA 001) + the country code + phone number (including the area code, without the initial '0', where there is one). If you wish to send a fax, you may do so from most hotels, though the charge may seem high.

reverse-charge call	**paga pelo destinatário**
Can you get me this number in …?	**Pode ligar-me para este número em …?**

TIME ZONES (local)

Portugal, being at the western edge of Europe, maintains GMT (along with the UK) and is therefore 1 hour behind the rest of the EU. From the last Sunday in March until the last Sunday in October, the clocks are moved 1 hour ahead for summer time (GMT +1).

TIPPING (serviço; gorjeta)

Hotel and restaurant bills are generally all-inclusive, but an additional tip of 5–10 percent is expected in restaurants. Hotel porters, per bag, generally receive €0.50–1. Give hairdressers, tour guides and taxi drivers around 10 percent.

TOILETS (WC; quarto de banho; serviços)

Public toilets exist in some large towns, but almost every bar and restaurant has one available for public use. Large hotels are also an excellent place to find clean toilets. While it's polite to buy a coffee or drink if you drop in to use the restroom, no one will shout at you for not doing so.

The Ladies' is marked *Senhoras* and the Gentlemen's *Homens*.

TOURIST INFORMATION *(turismo)*

Information on the Algarve may be obtained from Portuguese National Tourist Offices (ICEP, or *Investimentos, Comércio e Turismo de Portugal*) in many countries:

Canada: Suite 1005, 60 Bloor Street West, Toronto, Ontario M4W 3B8; tel: 416-921 7376.

Ireland: 54 Dawson Street, Dublin 2; tel: 353-1670 9133.

South Africa: 4th floor, Sunnyside Ridge, Sunnyside Drive, Parktown. PO Box 2473 Houghton, Johannesburg; tel: 2711-484 3487.

United Kingdom: 11 Belgrave Square, London SW1X 8PP; tel: 020-7201 6666.

USA: 590 Fifth Ave, 4th floor, New York, NY 10036; tel: 212-719 3985.

In the Algarve itself, all major (and some minor) towns have tourist information offices, staffed by helpful English-speaking assistants. Always make the *turismo* your first stop and pick up the town map/brochure (printed in several languages), which locates all major points of interest. The major Algarve regional office is in Faro (Av. 5 de Outubro, 18; tel: 289-800 400 or 289-800 477). Others include:

Albufeira: Rua 5 de Outubro; tel: 289-585 279

Faro airport: tel: 289-818 582

Lagos: Rua Vasco da Gama; tel: 282-763 031

Portimão: Av. Zeca Afonso; tel: 282-416 556

Praia da Rocha: Av. Tomás Cabreira; tel: 282-419 132

Sagres: Rua Comandante Matoso-Vila do Bispo; tel: 282-624 873

W

WEBSITES AND INTERNET CAFÉS

Websites worth checking before you go include:

• <www.algarve.org> Official website for the Algarve region.

• <www.cp.pt> Caminhos de Ferro Portugueses, national railway network, with timetables and details of international and domestic trains.

• **<www.portugalgolf.pt>**; **<www.algarvegolf.net>** Sites on golf, with information specifically related to the Algarve.

• **<www.portugal.org>** Portuguese Tourism Office.

• **<www.portugalvirtual.pt>** General country information and tourism database, with accommodation links.

• **<www.pousadas.pt>** Government-owned inns of Portugal.

• **<www.rtalgarve.pt>** Algarve regional tourism office.

• **<www.tap.pt>** TAP/Air Portugal – the Portuguese national airline.

Internet cafés. Most resorts have at least one internet café or computer centre where visitors can access e-mail for a small hourly fee. Check with the local tourist information office, as these tend to come and go with regularity. In Albufeira, visit the Goldspot Internet Café (Rua Alves Correira 81, in front of the Hotel Paraiso; open daily 10am to late; tel: 289-585 0884; <www.goldspot.pt>).

WEIGHTS AND MEASURES

The metric system is used in Portugal.

Y

YOUTH HOSTELS *(pousadas de juventude)*

Five youth hostels operate year-round in the Algarve:

Alcoutim: tel: 281-546 004; 54 beds

Faro: Rua de PSP – Edifício do IPJ; tel: 289-826 521; 54 beds

Lagos: Rua de Lançarote de Freitas, 50; tel: 282-761 970; 62 beds

Portimão: Lugar da Coca Maravilhas; tel: 282-491 804; 180 beds

Vila Real de Santo António: Rua Dr Manuel Cardona, Edificio do IPJ; tel: 259-373 193; 76 beds

For additional information, contact the headquarters of the Portuguese Youth Hostel Association (Associação Portuguesa de Pousadas de Juventude), Rua Lúcio de Azevedo Nr 27, 1600-146; tel: 21-723 2100; <www.pousadasjuventude.pt>.

Recommended Hotels

Visitors have a vast range of accommodation options in this part of Portugal. Hotels are scattered across the major towns and resorts of the Algarve, but densely clustered in sprawling resorts that stretch from Lagos to Faro–especially around Portimão, Albufeira and Vilamoura.

Book well in advance for high season, July–September, when hotel beds are difficult to come by. Hotel prices are hugely inflated in the height and heat of summer (though many luxury hotels are also at peak rates around Christmas and New Year). A hotel that is a relatively good bargain in May or October – in many ways the best time to visit the Algarve – may be prohibitively overpriced during the summer months.

Room price guidelines below are *rack rates* for a double room with bath in *high* season, including breakfast and value-added tax. Thus, the prices below may be considerably more than you'll end up paying. All hotels, save for the tiniest residential inns, accept major credit cards. For making reservations, Portugal's country code is 351; the prefixes for the Algarve are 281, 282 and 289.

€€€€€	over €230
€€€€	€140–230
€€€	€90–140
€€	€60–90
€	under €60

SAGRES

Aparthotel Navigator €€ *Rua Infante D. Henrique, Sagres; tel: 282-624 354; fax: 282-624 360; <www.hotel-navigator. com>*. This modern hotel, on a cliff right next to the *pousada (see below)*, has basic apartments built around a nice central swimming pool. A good deal for guests who enjoy the low-key, unglitzy appeal of Sagres. Off-season it's an especially good deal. Wheelchair-accessible. 55 apartments.

Hotel da Baleeira €€€ *Vila de Sagres; tel: 282-624 212; fax: 282-624 425; <www.sagres.net/baleeira>*. A large, good-value hotel overlooking the colourful Sagres harbour and within easy striking distance of several sheltered beaches. Simple rooms, nice pool. Sea-view rooms slightly more expensive. 120 rooms.

Pousada do Infante €€€€ *Ponta da Atalaia, 8650 Sagres; tel: 282-620 240; fax: 282-642 225; <www.pousadas.pt>*. Clinging to a rocky cliff looking out across the Atlantic, this *pousada* (one of just two along the Algarve) is prized for its location. Rooms are somewhat austere, but most have terraces with excellent views to the coast. 51 rooms.

BURGAU

Casa Grande € *Burgau; tel: 282-697 416; fax: 282-697 825; <www.nexus-pt.com/casagrande>*. Unique accomodation in a rambling old villa above the slow-moving fishing village of Burgau. Charismatic Sally Vincent, an ex-actress, has been running it since 1972 and will provide you with all you need to know about the region. 7 rooms.

LAGOS

Albergaria Casa de São Gonçalo €€ *Rua Cândido dos Reis 73, Lagos; tel: 282-762 171; fax: 282-763 927*. This fine 18th-century mansion in the heart of old Lagos has stone staircases that lead to rooms and landings filled with antiques. There is a lovely, plant-ringed interior patio and lounge. Closed in winter. 13 rooms.

Dom Pedro Meia Praia Beach Club €€€ *Meia Praia, Lagos; tel: 289-300 780; fax: 289-381 001; <www.dompedro.pt>*. This large and popular aparthotel is just across the road from one of the longest stretches of sand along the Algarve coast: Meia Praia, the closest beach to Lagos (3km/2 miles) from town. Well-equipped, airy apartments. Two swimming pools, two tennis courts, mini-golf and landscaped gardens. Good roster of activities and golfing discounts. Wheelchair-accessible. 66 rooms.

Tivoli Lagos €€€€ *António Crisógono Santos, Lagos; tel: 282-761 020; fax: 282-790 345; <www.tivolihotels.com>.* An excellent choice for those who would prefer to stay in a hotel with character and style in old Lagos rather than on the beach in a generic seaside hotel. Handsome and colourful rooms, attractive poolside areas, indoor swimming pool, fitness centre, tennis courts, plus water sports at the Duna Beach Club (hotel transport arranged). Wheelchair-accessible. 319 rooms.

PORTIMÃO AND ENVIRONS

Hotel Bela Vista €€€ *Avenida Tomás Cabreira, Praia da Rocha, Portimão; tel: 282-450 480; fax: 282-415 369; <www.hotelbelavista.com>.* The first hotel in the Algarve, this free-standing mansion overlooks the beach and looks wholly out of place on very built-up Praia da Rocha. An architectural gem, resembling a church more than a hotel, the Bela Vista was built as a summer house in 1916. Its interior features beautiful wood ceilings and staircases, plus splendid 19th-century *azulejos*. First-floor rooms have large balconies; only two rooms, less desirable, have views of the unattractive beach town at the back. 14 rooms.

Hotel Oriental €€€€ *Avenida Tomás Cabreira, Praia da Rocha, Portimão; tel: 282-480 000; fax: 282-413 413.* In the more upscale (and slightly more tranquil) end of Praia da Rocha, this Moorish fantasy palace was designed in the style of the casino that stood on this spot in the 1920s. Features a galleried interior, Turkish bath, pretty gardens with sun terraces, and swimming pools looking onto the beach. Wheelchair-accessible. 85 rooms.

Le Méridien Penina €€€€–€€€€€ *Montes de Alvor, Portimão; tel: 282-420 200; fax: 282-420 300; <www.lemeridien-penina. com>.* The original luxury golf resort on the Algarve is set within a 145-hectare (360-acre) estate, which includes the world-famous Penina golf course. Perfect for the well-heeled sports lover, with floodlit tennis, sailing, windsurfing, horse riding and a gym. 196 rooms.

Residencial Praia do Vau €€ *Portimão; tel: 282-401 312; fax: 282-401 756.* A small, rustic and comfortable inn in an attractive Algarvian house just 200m (650ft) from the Praia do Vau beach (west of Praia da Rocha). 21 rooms.

ALVOR

Hotel Dom João II €€€–€€€€ *Praia de Alvor, (1km/under a mile from Alvor); tel: 282-400 700; fax: 282-400 799; <www.pestana.com>.* A Pestana group hotel, this 7-storey complex is bright and airy with a large swimming pool and spacious sun terraces. Some rooms have sea views. A short walk from a tranquil beach. Part of the expansive Torralta tourist complex, which offers a wide range of sporting facilities, shopping and entertainment possibilities. 219 rooms.

Pestana Alvor Praia Hotel €€€€€ *Praia de Três Irmãos, Alvor; tel: 282-400 900; fax: 282-400 999; <www.pestana.com>.* This large and luxurious, recently refurbished hotel sits among thick trees and gardens on cliffs. It overlooks one of the finest beaches along the coast, Praia dos Três Irmãos, which is floodlit at night. Outdoor and indoor seawater pools. Three top-flight restaurants with terraces and different cuisines. Tennis courts, full spa. Wheelchair-accessible. 198 rooms.

CARVOEIRO

Hotel Carvoeiro Sol €€€€ *Praia do Carvoeiro, Lagoa; tel: 282-357 301; fax: 282-357 211; <www.carvoeirosol.com>.* Wedged right into the narrow opening between twin cliffs above Carvoeiro's tiny beach, this modern, comfortable hotel has a central courtyard, bar and restaurant, and clean, bright, beach-style rooms. Wheelchair-accessible. 54 rooms.

MONCHIQUE

Estalagem Abrigo da Montanha €€–€€€ *Estrada Monchique-Fóia, Monchique; tel: 282-912 131; fax: 282-913 660;*

<www.abrigodamontanha.com>. High up in the Serra de Monchique, away from the heat and crowds of the coast, this wood-and-granite mountain lodge is a special retreat. It's not luxurious, but it has style and spectacular views. Pretty rooftop swimming pool and café-restaurant across the road. Slightly more expensive rooms are larger and come with a bigger terrace. 16 rooms.

SILVES

Colina dos Mouros €€ *Pocinho Santo, Silves; tel: 282-440 420; fax: 282-440 426.* Located on the outskirts of Silves, this hotel has fine views of the fortress and attractively furnished, modern rooms. Landscaped gardens, restaurant, bar and swimming pool. 57 rooms.

ALBUFEIRA/FALÉSIA

Albufeira Jardim I & II €€ *Cerro da Piedade, Albufeira; tel: 289-570 070/090; fax: 289-570 071; <www.albufeira-jardim. com>.* A large enclosed complex of whitewashed tourist apartments sit on a hill overlooking the sea. They enjoy fine views and a quiet setting, only a 5-minute walk into town. With five pools, tennis courts, shopping, bars and supermarket. All apartments have either a balcony or terrace. Good value. Bus shuttle service to beach and Albufeira town. 470 apartments.

Alfagar Aldeamento Turístico €€€ *Santa Eulália, Albufeira; tel: 289-540 220; fax: 289-542 770; <www.alfagar.com>.* Very nicely landscaped gardens and a cliff-top walkway surround this good-value holiday apartment complex. One-, two- and three-bedroom apartments with cleaning service five days a week. Just a short walk to the beaches on either side. 220 apartments.

Hotel Apartamentos Ourapraia/Clube Praia da Oura €€€ *Areias São João, Albufeira; tel: 289-590 326; fax: 289-585 288; <www.clubepraiadaoura.com>.* An attractive holiday complex of well-equipped apartments centred around swimming pools. Tennis courts, sauna, children's playground and close proximity to the

Albufeira beach. Excellent value, especially during high season. 126 apartments.

Hotel Boa Vista €€€ *Rua Samora Barros 20, Albufeira; tel: 289-589 175; fax: 289-589 180; <www.hotelboavista.com>.* Superb setting, built into the cliff at the very western end of town, with a view over the whole of Albufeira. Close enough to walk to town but far enough away to be quiet in high season. Swimming pool and sun terrace. 93 rooms.

Hotel Falésia €€€ *Pinhal do Concelho, Praia da Falésia; tel: 289-501 237; fax: 289-501 270; <www.falesia.com>.* A modern hotel that looks like an apartment building on the edge of the Pine Cliffs resort and golf course. Garden-like lobby, pool with waterfall, some one- and two-bedroom apartments. Falésia beach access is through the adjacent Sheraton Algarve. Wheelchair-accessible. 145 rooms.

Hotel Sol e Mar €€€ *Rua José Bernadino de Sousa, Albufeira; tel: 289-580 080; fax: 289-587 036; <www.grupofbarata.com>.* A large block hotel in the town centre with somewhat dated rooms but good value given its main asset – it's built right into the cliff on Albufeira's desirable beach. Indoor pool. A popular economy package-tour hotel. 74 rooms.

Residencial Villa Recife €–€€ *Rua Miguel Bombarda, 6, Albufeira; tel: 289-586 747; fax: 289-587 182.* A 2-minute walk from the heart of old Albufeira, a converted private house with a pleasant garden entrance. The old section of the house has more character than the modern wing. 29 rooms.

Sheraton Algarve (Pine Cliffs) Hotel & Resort €€€€€ *Praia da Falésia, Albufeira; tel: 289-500 102; fax: 289-501 950; <www.luxurycollection.com>.* One of the Algarve's most distinguished and luxurious developments, surrounded by pines at the top of dramatic cliffs. Handsome Moorish styling, excellent restaurants and extensive sporting facilities, including nine-hole cliff-top golf course, tennis, semi-private beach, three pools and spa. Brand-new luxury 'Golf Suites', plus villas and apartments. Great facilities for children. Wheelchair-accessible. 215 rooms (33 suites, 70 apartments).

Vila Channa €€€ *São Rafael, Albufeira; tel: 289-592 354; fax: 289-591 597.* A nice, clean, villa-style small hotel a short walk from a couple of the prettiest beaches near Albufeira, Castelo and São Rafael. Nice pool. 18 rooms.

Vila Joya €€€€€ *Praia da Galé, Albufeira; tel: 289-591 795; fax: 289-591 201; <www.vilajoya.com>.* Probably the most stylish hotel on the entire coast, this sumptuously decorated small palazzo is full year-round. Ensconced in beautiful gardens, the Moorish-influenced villa is just minutes from the pretty, calm Galé beach. Beautiful bathrooms and public rooms. Most rooms have sea views. Lovely small pool. Reserve several months in advance. 17 rooms.

VILAMOURA

Dom Pedro Marina €€€€ *Rua Tivoli Lote H4, Vilamoura, Quarteira; tel: 289-381 000; fax: 289-381 001; <www.dompedro. com>.* Impressive hotel with a tropical feel – palm trees, wicker furniture, tile floors and bamboo shades – perched right on the edge of the Vilamoura marina. Nice gardens and swimming pool. Preferential terms for guests at local golf courses. Wheelchair-accessible. 262 rooms.

Hotel Atlantis Vilamoura €€€€ *Av. Oceano Atlantico, Vilamoura; tel: 289-381 600; fax: 289-389 962.* This very comfortable, modern hotel complex near the beach and marina has well-furnished rooms and four swimming pools. Discounts for guests playing golf at four nearby courses. Restaurants, bars, health club. 311 rooms.

Tivoli Marinotel €€€€€ *Vilamoura; tel: 289-303 303; fax: 289-303 345; <www.tivolihotels.com>.* Sandwiched between the marina and the beach, this hotel is the perfect metaphor for

Vilamoura resort: massive, slick and expensive. Like the resort, though, it also completes its aims very well. Great views, ultra-modern lobby, very good restaurants, state-of-the-art facilities, tennis courts and indoor and outdoor pools to pamper guests. Wheelchair-accessible. 389 rooms.

VALE DO LOBO

Le Méridien Dona Filipa €€€€€ *Vale do Lobo; tel: 289-357 200; fax: 289-357 201; <www.lemeridien.com>.* A handsomely appointed hotel that's a favourite of Algarve golfers. Set amid 180 hectares (450 acres), part of the exclusive Vale do Lobo resort, it has elegant traditional rooms and public areas, plus a gambling room. Green fees at the excellent San Lorenzo golf course included. Three floodlit tennis courts. Good golf packages available. Wheelchair-accessible. 147 rooms.

QUINTA DO LAGO

Hotel Quinta do Lago €€€€€ *Quinta do Lago, Almancil; tel: 289-350 350; fax: 289-394 905; <www.quintadolagohotel. com>.* One of the standard bearers for luxury and leisure in the Algarve, this Orient Express hotel is set amid 800 hectares (2,000 acres) of gardens and woods. Rooms are tastefully and elegantly decorated. Three golf courses wend their fairways through the Ria Formosa Nature Preserve and are among the finest in Europe. Water sports, health club, pools and beach access across lovely wooden bridge. Distinguished service. Wheelchair-accessible. 141 rooms.

FARO

Hotel Eva €€€€ *Avenida da República, 1, Faro; tel: 289-001 000; fax: 289-001 002; <www.tdhotels.pt>.* The biggest hotel in Faro, the Eva is a large, modern block on the edge of the harbour 90m (100yds) from pedestrian shopping streets and the old town. Three bars, two restaurants and rooftop swimming pool. Wheelchair-accessible. 150 rooms.

Hotel Faro €€€ *Praça Dom Francisco Gomes, 2, Faro; tel: 289-830 830; fax: 289-830 829.* This hotel was revamped from the ground up in 2000. Now part of Faro's swankiest shopping centre, the hotel is ideally placed – just outside the old town and overlooking a lively plaza and the harbour – and appealingly chic. Wheelchair-accessible. 52 rooms.

SAO BRAS DE ALPORTEL

Pousada de São Brás €€€€ *São Brás de Alportel; tel: 289-842 305; fax: 289-841 726; <www.pousadas.pt>.* A quiet manor house with magnificent views of both the surrounding mountains and the sea a half hour away. This was the first *pousada* built in the Algarve, in 1942, and the second in all Portugal. Restaurant, bar, tennis court and swimming pool. A good place to get away from the sunbathing masses to relax. 41 rooms.

TAVIRA

Casa do Rio €€ *António Afonso, 39, Tavira; tel: 281-326 578.* Small and characterful bed and breakfast in a private home with a pool right on the river in historic Tavira. Minimum stay three nights. No credit cards. 5 rooms.

Convento de São António €€ *Rua de Santo António, 56, Tavira; tel/fax: 281-325 632.* This small, family-owned hotel was a monastery in the 17th century. The elegantly appointed rooms are certainly much more comfortable than they once were as monks' cells. Attractive swimming pool and central patio. Minimum stay required. 7 rooms.

O Pequeno Castelo € *Poço das Bruxas, Santo Estavão, Tavira; tel/fax: 281-961 692; email: pequenocastelo@hotmail.com>.* On the outskirts of picturesque town of Tavira, 'the little castle' is a quiet and friendly bed and breakfast with views of the Atlantic from the veranda. Well placed for walks in the countryside. Swimming pool. Minimum stay of four nights. 4 rooms and apartment (on request).

Recommended Restaurants

For most visitors, dining in the Algarve is still limited to hotel food and the occasional café-snack bar in town or on the beach. There are plenty of very good restaurants in the major towns and resorts, but there are also many that seem far more intent on separating tourists from their euros than offering genuine Algarvian and Portuguese food. The guide below should help you find more authentic eating experiences.

The prices indicated are for starter, main course and dessert, with wine, per person. (Note that some fish or shellfish dishes, charged by the kilo, will be more expensive than the averages.) Service and value-added tax of 12 percent are included, as they generally are in the bill. Except where noted, all restaurants accept major credit cards.

Prices normally include taxes and a service charge, but it is customary to leave an additional 5–10 percent tip for good service.

€€€€	over €40
€€€	€25–40
€€	€15–25
€	under €15

SAGRES

A Tasca €€–€€€ *Porto de Sagres; tel: 282-624 177.* Open daily for lunch and dinner. This restaurant is one of the best in Sagres for fresh seafood. Choose to dine on the sun-scorched outdoor terrace that overlooks the harbour or in the dark stone interior. Both serve the same great sea bass, lobster and grilled squid kebabs.

Vila Velha €€–€€€ *Ponta da Atalaia; tel: 282-624 788.* Open Tues–Sun for lunch and dinner. Just down the road from the *pousada*, the husband-and-wife team that operates this attractive rustic restaurant serve large portions of traditional Portuguese dishes. The daily *ementa*, or fixed-price menu, for two is a good deal.

LAGOS

A Lagosteira €€ *Rua 1 Maio, 20; tel: 282-762 486.* Open daily except lunch Sat and Sun. This long-established simple restaurant is centrally located and serves good, imaginative seafood. The fish *cataplana* is particularly good. Some outdoor tables.

Cervejaria-Grill Arribalé €€ *Rua da Barroca, 40; tel: 282-761 303.* Open daily for dinner. This cute, tiny tavern specialises in fresh grilled fish. There are only a few tables inside, but customers spill out on to a narrow street in the old quarter.

Dom Sebastião €€€ *Rua 25 de Abril 20–22; tel: 282-762 795.* Open daily for lunch and dinner (closed Sun in winter). On Lagos's main pedestrian thoroughfare, this very popular, rustic-style restaurant with dark beams focuses on live seafood. It also has outdoor tables.

Escondidinho €–€€ *Beco do Cemitério; tel: 282-760 386.* Open Mon–Sat for lunch and dinner. A typical, family restaurant where grilled fish is the speciality, and the cooking is done in front of the customers. Traditional *cataplanas* (fish or meat) are also recommended.

MONCHIQUE–FOIA

Abrigo da Montanha €€–€€€ *Estrada da Fóia; tel: 282-912 131.* Open daily for lunch and dinner. One of several good roadside restaurants with terraces enjoying panoramic views. Try the *frango piri-piri* (spicy chicken), which comes in mountainous portions to echo the view; or the *cataplana*.

PORTIMAO AND ENVIRONS

A Lanterna €€ *Rua Foz do Arade, Porchal; tel: 282-414 429.* Open Mon–Sat for dinner. On the Ferragudo side of the Portimão Bridge, this long-established restaurant has a reputation for high quality, with elegant dining in small, traditionally furnished rooms. Specials include smoked fish and some interesting desserts.

Dona Barca €–€€ *Largo da Barca; tel: 282-484 189.* Open daily for lunch and dinner. This fish restaurant has an excellent reputation for quality fresh food and typical Algarvian cuisine – it has even represented the region at various national gastronomic festivals. The dining room is pleasant, with stone walls and draped fishing nets.

PRAIA DA ROCHA

A Casa da Rocha €€–€€€ *Sítio dos Castelos, Av. Tomás Cabreira; tel: 282-419 674.* Open daily for lunch and dinner. If it's a restaurant with a view you're after, you could hardly do better than this place, in an airy summer beach house with three terraces and consummate panoramic views of the ocean. Sunset dinners are understandably popular. Choose from Portuguese *couverts* (appetisers) and grilled fish and meats.

Churrasqueira da Rocha €€€ *Avenida Tomás Cabreira; tel: 282-417 452.* Open daily for lunch and dinner. *Churrasqueira* means grill, and you can get lots of grilled meats – including the famous *espetadas*, or kebabs – and the house speciality, chicken *piri-piri*, at this large place with good views of the beach.

Safari €–€€ *Rua António Feu; tel: 282-423 540.* Open daily for lunch and dinner. This sea-view restaurant combines good Portuguese cuisine with a distinctive Angolan flavour.

PRAIA DE TRÊS IRMÃOS/ALVOR

Búzios €€€ *Aldeamento Turístico de Prainha, Praia de Três Irmãos; tel: 282-458 772.* Open daily for dinner. Ensconced in a beach community of white houses and condos, a short walk from the shoreline, this chic restaurant has an appealing terrace and international menu (including traditional Portuguese cuisine). Good wine list.

Restaurante Ababuja €€–€€€ *Rua da Ribeira; tel: 282-458 979.* Open daily for lunch and dinner (except Wed lunch). Situated on the waterfront, near the fish market, this family-run restaurant has simple décor and friendly service. Not surprisingly, it's well

known for its fresh fish and seafood but does unusual specialities
including stuffed squid and cuttlefish with beans. The catch of the
day is always a good bet.

ALBUFEIRA

A Ruina €€–€€€ *Cais Herculano; tel: 289-512 094.* Open daily
for lunch and dinner. A 19th-century, four-storey mansion, 'the
Ruin' features a basic dining room downstairs, rustic-looking
restaurant on the second floor and roof-top dining with views over
Praia dos Pescadores. Near the fish market and just west of
'Fishermen's Beach', the speciality is well-prepared seafood. Try
the *caldeirada* (fish stew).

La Cigale €€€ *Praia de Olhos d' Água; tel: 289-501 637.* Open
daily for lunch and dinner. Excellent seafood in a rustic, whitewashed beachside restaurant with an attractive terrace. Perfect for
lazy and informal eating by day, La Cigale is elegant and romantic
by night. Try the *mollusc a la cigale*, a shellfish special.

Paulu's Pizzeria € *Edifício Oura Cláudios, Estrada da Santa
Eulália, Albufeira; tel: 289-587 159.* Open daily noon–11pm. A good
place for a family meal out with good pizzas and pastas and children's
menus. Alfresco and conservatory dining. Take-away available.

Restaurante do Hotel Vila Joya €€€€ *in Hotel Vila Joya, Praia
de Galé; tel: 289-591 795.* Open daily for lunch and dinner; closed
mid-Nov–early Mar. The restaurant of the most luxurious and
sumptuously designed small hotel along the Algarve is, like the
hotel, refined and elegant. To suit its multi-national patrons, the
kitchen prepares eclectic international dishes. Reservations for
non-guests essential.

Restaurante Marisqueira €€€ *Praia de Santa Eulália; tel: 289-
542 636.* Open daily for dinner. If you arrive early, you'll be
rewarded with a window seat and excellent views over Santa
Eulália beach to accompany quality Algarvian cooking. Fresh fish
and seafood specialities.

GUIA

O Teodósio € *Estrada Algoz, Guia; tel: 289-561 318*. Open daily for lunch and dinner. Guia is renowned for its chicken *piri-piri* dishes and this hugely popular restaurant is known as the Rei do Frango (King of Chicken). Be prepared for queues and crowded, communal tables.

AROUND ALMANCIL

Casa Velha €€€€ *Quinta do Lago, Almancil; tel: 289-394 983*. Open Mon–Sat for dinner. The elegant resort that's grown up around it has only recently caught up to the chic standards set by this restaurant for nearly three decades. In a renovated 19th-century farmhouse (hence the name, 'old house'), this is about as elegant as dining in the Algarve gets. The French menu is sophisticated, the dishes artfully prepared and the service perfect, but it's not at all stuffy. Excellent wine cellar.

Gigi Beach €€€ *Quinta do Lago; tel: 09-404 5178*. Open daily for lunch. The setting is simple: a wooden beach shack tucked in among the dunes and wetlands of the Ria Formosa Nature Preserve, reached across a long wooden bridge. The food is also simple: point to the fish of your choice and watch it taken directly to the grill.

Pequeno Mundo €€€ *Pereiras (Almancil, just off Estrada de Quarteira); tel: 289-399 866*. Open Mon–Sat for dinner. In a charming setting of renovated cottages, gourmet-standard French and international cuisine is prepared by an English proprietor. Favourites are the fish stew and the Chateaubriand, served with Béarnaise sauce. Terrace and indoor dining.

Restaurante Ermitage €€€€ *Estrada Almancil-Vale do Lobo; tel: 289-355 271*. Open Tues–Sun for dinner. The Dutch duo behind this ancient farmhouse-turned-elegant-restaurant have created a treat for their international clientele of expatriates and upmarket visitors to the Quinta do Lago and Vale do Lobo resort area. The creative menu, which uses the freshest ingredients, changes seasonally.

VILAMOURA

Restaurante O Cesteiro €€€ *Estrada de Falésia-Vilamoura; tel: 289-312 961.* Open Thur–Tues for lunch and dinner. This terrace restaurant overlooks the glittering Vilamoura marina, so you can ponder the yachts as you sample charcoal-grilled fish and seafood items.

Restaurante Pier One €€€ *Clube Náutico, Marina da Vilamoura; tel: 289-322 734.* Open daily for dinner; closed Mon in winter. With a terrace that offers panoramic views of the marina and, in the distance, the sea, Pier One is a tempting place for alfresco dining at sunset. Interesting selections, such as Mozambican prawns, monkfish lasagne and chicken, and bananas in a puff pastry.

FARO

A Tasca €€–€€€ *Rua do Alportel, 38; tel: 289-824 739.* Open Mon–Sat for lunch and dinner. This small simple restaurant serves unusual and authentic Algarvian fare. Excellent selection of wines.

Dois Irmãos €€ *Largo do Terreiro do Bispo 18; tel: 289-823 337.* The Two Brothers restaurant has been a Faro seafood legend since as long ago as 1925. This simple bistro has an extensive fish menu, including nine types of *cataplana*, and lots of regional specials.

Mesa dos Mouros €€–€€€ *Largo da Sé; tel: 289-878 873.* Open Mon–Sat for lunch and dinner. A friendly place with a terrace in the shadow of the cathedral in the heart of Faro's old town, 'The Moors' Table' is a good place for a sightseeing break during the day and a simple lunch of grilled sardines.

TAVIRA

Quatro Águas €€€ *Sítio das Quatro Aguas; tel: 281-325 329.* Open daily for lunch and dinner; closed Mon in winter. This handsome 18th-century building on the harbour is a fine choice for a seafood meal. Traditional Portuguese dining, with an emphasis on dishes such as *arroz de marisco* (seafood rice), *cataplana* and octopus chowder.

INDEX